Nature Library

BIRDS

Nature Library

BIRDS

John Andrews

Exeter Books

NEW YORK

Artists

David Andrews, Norman Arlott, John Barber, John Busby,
Peter Hayman, The Hayward Art Group, Ken Lilly, Linden
Artists Limited, Peter Morter & Design Bureau, Robert Morton,
Pat Oxenham, Denys Ovenden, John Rignall, Arthur Singer,
Maurice Wilson, Ian Willis.

Copyright © Newnes Books 1983
London · New York · Sydney · Toronto
Astronaut House, Hounslow Road, Feltham, Middlesex, England

First published in USA 1983 by Exeter Books
Distributed by Bookthrift
Exeter is a trademark of Simon & Schuster
Bookthrift is a registered trademark of Simon & Schuster
New York, New York

ISBN 0-671-05593-3

Printed in Italy

Photographic acknowledgements

ARDEA PHOTOGRAPHICS, LONDON 68,
J. Carlson 27, M.D. England 18 bottom, Kenneth W. Fink 29, Valerie Taylor 69 bottom, W. R. Taylor 20: BRITISH MUSEUM, LONDON 13; BRUCE COLEMAN, UXBRIDGE: 21 bottom, 55 top, 63 top, Jen and Des Bartlett 66 – 67, S.C. Bisserot 18 top, Alain Compost 40, Stephen Dalton 10, Peter Davey 62, L. R. Dawson 11, A. J. Deane 50, C. Duscher 54 bottom, Robert Gillmor 6 – 7, Leonard Lee Rue 37, John Pearson 56, G. D. Plage 19, Joe Van Wormer 35 bottom, G. Ziesler 17; ADRIAN DAVIES, WALLINGTON 69 top; RON EASTMAN 15; P. J. GREEN, LONDON 9; HAMLYN GROUP PICTURE LIBRARY 24 – 25, 46, 76 – 77; BRIAN HAWKES, NEWNHAM 26, 51; ERIC HOSKING, LONDON 35 top, 55 bottom, Naill Rankin 11 top; JACANA PRESS AGENCY, PARIS: Alain Lagurgue 75, Montoya 22, Nardin 58, 59, Ziesler 71; FRANK LANE, PINNER 43; S. D. MACDONALD 31 top; NATIONAL AUDOBON SOCIETY, NEW YORK 22; NATURAL HISTORY PHOTOGRAPHIC AGENCY, HYTHE: A. Bannister 54 top, E. A. Janes 32, Peter Johnson 52, K. B. Newman 57, M. Savonius 28, Philippa Scott 16; SCOTT SWEDBERG, WEST MILLBURY, MASSACHUSETS 49 top; P. O. SWANBERG, SCARABORSGATAN, 33; WEHA-PHOTO, BERNE 60; WILDLIFE SERVICE, NEW ZEALAND 67 top.

Contents

Introduction

Birds are not only one of the most successful groups in the animal kingdom but they hold a special position in our awareness of the natural world. They are often the most obvious living creatures in a landscape (their apparent confidence borne of an ability to fly to safety) and their bright colours and melodic songs have long been admired by man, yet it is only recently that we have begun to fully appreciate just how intricate their lives are.

The 8000 species of bird have evolved over millions of years and have adapted to many different modes of life. If one was to take a single feature which places the birds apart from all other animals it would be the development of feathers. These complex and delicate structures not only make flight possible but also serve many other functions, notably providing insulation from cold or wet and furnishing attractive or eye-catching plumages for use in courtship and territorial rituals.

The following pages introduce the basic biology of the bird.

Lesser flamingoes feeding in the dawn mist at Lake Nakuru, Kenya. The population of lesser flamingo on this one lake has been estimated at over one million birds, out of a world population of five to six million.

Evolution and antiquity

Birds have lived on earth for far longer than man or any of the mammals. When giant dinosaurs roamed the world, there were already many kinds of birds inhabiting the forests, the wetlands and the marine environment. They included some types which we would recognise today, such as grebes, herons and waterfowl. In fact, it seems that birds are probably descended from small dinosaurs called coelurosaurs which ran standing up on their hind legs and balancing with their tails, much as birds do today. *Compsognathus (below)* is a typical coelurosaur.

The birds' reptilian ancestors were cold-blooded, active only when the heat of the sun had warmed up their bodies and becoming torpid at night or in cold weather. Obviously, any creature which

The fossil remains of the earliest bird-like creatures known to science – *Archaeopteryx* (the name means 'old wings') – were found in Germany in sediments which are about 150 million years old. Its pigeon-sized skeleton is much more like a reptile than like a modern bird: it has a jaw with teeth instead of a beak; there are claws on its fingers; it has a long bony tail and it lacks the strong breastbone which, in true birds, supports the powerful muscles needed for proper flight. But it does have long feathers on its forelimbs, like the primary wing feathers of modern birds, and all down its tail. Whether or not it could fly at all is anyone's guess – perhaps it only glided from tree to tree in calm air or just trotted along the ground using its wings as a

sort of butterfly net to help it catch small insects to eat, with its feathery tail helping it to keep its balance. What is certain is that the few fossil skeletons of this sharp-toothed little monster from the swamps of prehistoric Bavaria are our main clue to the direct link between the reptiles and the familiar sparrows and starlings which live around us today.

Unfortunately, because birds are small and their bones are light, their remains are not often found as fossils, but from the discoveries that have been made we know that 100 million years ago true birds had evolved with their skeletons adapted for powered and controlled flight. By the Eocene period, 60 million years ago, many of the modern families of birds had already appeared as well as

	Millions of years	Ratites	Tinamous	Grebes	Divers	Penguins	Tube-nosed swimmers	Pelicans and allies	Herons and flamingos	Waterfowl	Hawks, eagles, vultures	Chicken-like birds	Cranes, rails and allies	Waders, gulls, auks	Doves, parrots, cuckoos	Owls and goatsuckers	Swifts and humming-birds	Climbing birds, rollers, etc.	Perching birds	Man
PLEISTOCENE																				
PLIOCENE	10																			
MIOCENE	20																			
	30																			
OLIGOCENE	40																			
EOCENE	50																			
	60																			
PALEOCENE	70																			
UPPER CRETACEOUS	80																			
	90																			
	100																			

Above: **The relative age of some different orders of birds and of man.**

could make itself less dependent on warm external temperatures could be active, hunting or breeding, when cold-blooded competitors were immobilised. That would mean evolving an insulating coat so that heat generated by the digestion of food could be kept in the body to fuel the muscles – in other words, becoming warm-blooded. It is possible that some coelurosaurs developed loose, overlapping scales which helped to insulate them, and in turn these scales evolved into feathers (which are a very efficient insulation). The new, warm-blooded creatures which possessed them eventually began to use their feathers for other purposes, growing wings and tails like *Archaeopteryx*, and finally obtaining the power of true flight.

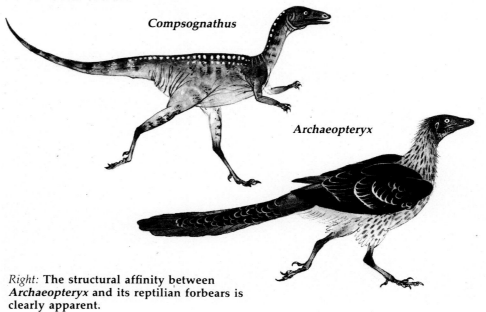

Compsognathus

Archaeopteryx

Right: **The structural affinity between *Archaeopteryx* and its reptilian forbears is clearly apparent.**

some extinct species such as *Diatryma* – a feasome, fast-running predator.

Birds are one of the most successful groups of creatures ever to exist. Today, there are more than 8000 different species that live in extremely different environments all over the world. One and all, they owe their success to the long-extinct reptile which grew feathers.

Diatryma, the 'terror crane', was a flightless predator almost 2 metres tall that lived on the North American plains 60 million years ago.

Archaeopteryx lithographica, the first bird, is known only from a few fossilized specimens found in the Jurassic limestone of Bavaria. The tail, bone structure and teeth resemble a small dinosaur, but the fine deposits have preserved the impression of the wing and tail feathers.

Feathers and flight

Birds have several sorts of feathers. Those used for flying are long and each is supported by a strong central shaft. In flight, as the bird beats its wings downward, the flexible tips of the feathers twist so that they are pushing air backwards and driving the bird itself forwards, operating in the same way as the twist in an aeroplane propellor. The tail helps to steer and balance the bird's flight. When it comes to land, a bird uses wing and tail like a parachute, spreading and pushing them forwards to break its momentum.

The bird's body and the bases of the flight and tail feathers are covered by smaller contour feathers which provide

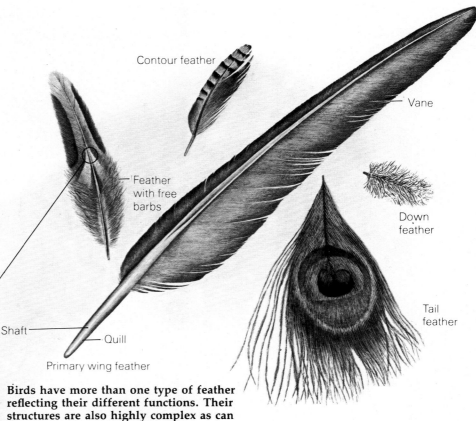

Contour feather

Vane

Feather with free barbs

Down feather

Shaft

Quill

Primary wing feather

Tail feather

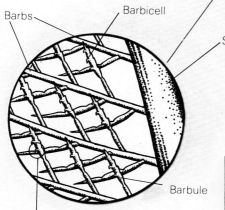

Barbs

Barbicell

Barbule

Hook of lower barbule locks in trough of upper barbule

Birds have more than one type of feather reflecting their different functions. Their structures are also highly complex as can be seen in the detail shown left.

a smooth outer coat and also protect it against injury, keep out water, and cover an 'underwear' of little downy feathers which hold air and trap warmth. When birds are cold, they fluff up their plumage to increase the thickness of this insulated layer. When they are warm, they sleek down their feathers to make their 'clothing' thinner. Lacking sweat glands, they may also pant to get cool.

Feathers are complex structures, combining strength with lightness and flexibility. They are made up of many tiny hooked barbs that zip together and birds spend much time meticulously preening their plumage to keep it in good repair. The head and face can only to preened by scratching with the feet and in many species, gentle mutual grooming of the head is an important part of their courtship. Many species bathe frequently even in the coldest weather, when, of course, good insulation is especially important.

Even with the best of care, plumage eventually becomes worn or damaged, so birds periodically moult out and renew their feathers to keep themselves in the best condition for flight and survival.

Coming in to land, a gannet uses wings and tail as air brakes to stop its forward motion before lowering its feet to the ground.

Below: A hen cuban finch preens her mate: an important part of courtship.

A bathing robin may look dejected, but clean plumage is essential for survival in cold weather.

Opposite: **Taking-off, the starling beats strongly down with its wings, the primary feathers spreading and twisting against the air to propel it forward**

Structure and skeleton

Birds' skeletons, respiratory and digestive systems and eyesight have all had to change greatly from their reptilian origins in order to create an efficient flying machine.

The flexible reptile skeleton has been largely fused together to form a strong box frame able to withstand the stresses caused by take-off and landing, by sudden changes of direction and by flying in turbulent air. To reduce their weight, birds' bones are hollow and, in some of the larger wing and leg bones, the interior is criss-crossed by many bracing struts: modern engineering practice shows that this sort of construction combines lightness with exceptional strength and flexibility, thus reducing the risk of breakage – a bird with a broken wing is soon a dead bird.

Flight uses energy, which in turn generates heat. Birds need very efficient respiration both to provide the oxygen necessary for converting stored fat into muscle power and to keep them cool. Connected to their lungs is a complex array of air sacs which extends through the body and into the bones, particularly to keep the working muscles from overheating and seizing up.

Any flying machine is easier to control if the bulk of the weight is at the centre of its body. So birds have had to make their heads as light as possible and they have done this by dispensing with teeth

Tawny Owl

Woodcock

■ binocular vision
▨ monocular vision
□ out of vision

House Sparrow

The angle of vision in birds. Binocular vision, which is needed to judge distance accurately, is essential for safe flight, and to predators: all-round vision is important for creatures which are hunted by others.

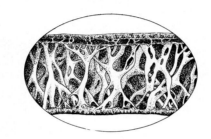

Internal struts give wing bones lightness and great strength.

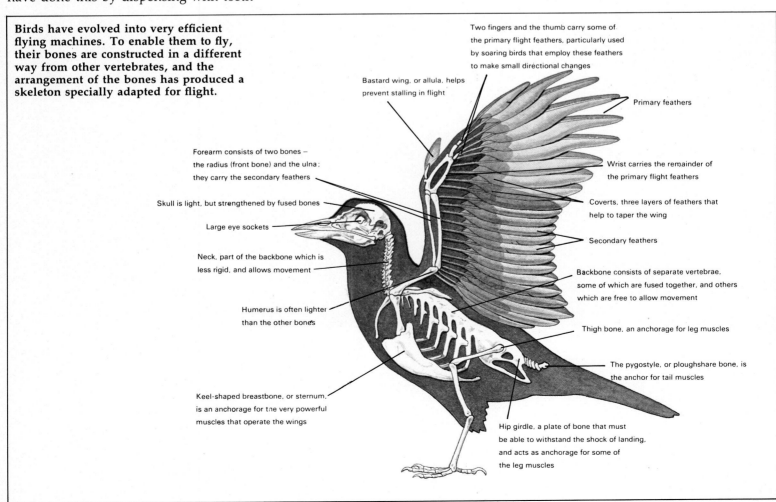

Birds have evolved into very efficient flying machines. To enable them to fly, their bones are constructed in a different way from other vertebrates, and the arrangement of the bones has produced a skeleton specially adapted for flight.

Two fingers and the thumb carry some of the primary flight feathers, particularly used by soaring birds that employ these feathers to make small directional changes

Bastard wing, or allula, helps prevent stalling in flight

Primary feathers

Forearm consists of two bones – the radius (front bone) and the ulna; they carry the secondary feathers

Wrist carries the remainder of the primary flight feathers

Skull is light, but strengthened by fused bones

Coverts, three layers of feathers that help to taper the wing

Large eye sockets

Secondary feathers

Neck, part of the backbone which is less rigid, and allows movement

Backbone consists of separate vertebrae, some of which are fused together, and others which are free to allow movement

Humerus is often lighter than the other bones

Thigh bone, an anchorage for leg muscles

The pygostyle, or ploughshare bone, is the anchor for tail muscles

Keel-shaped breastbone, or sternum, is an anchorage for the very powerful muscles that operate the wings

Hip girdle, a plate of bone that must be able to withstand the shock of landing, and acts as anchorage for some of the leg muscles

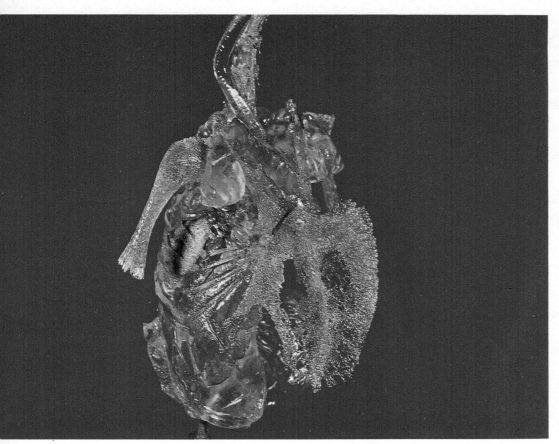

Cast of a pigeon's air sacs. Unique to birds, these aid respiration and cooling when muscles are working hard.

and all the associated heavy bones and muscles. Instead, they have a lightweight beak and they chew up their food internally. Swallowed whole or in large chunks, the food is first stored in the crop and then passed on to the gizzard. This is a tough, muscular bag which grinds up food items. Many kinds of bird deliberately swallow small pieces of grit which lodge in the gizzard and help the grinding process. One extra advantage of this system of digestion is that birds can take food from unsafe places, where they may be exposed to predators, gulping it down quickly to 'chew' it later in some places of safety.

Flight demands very good eyesight. Birds' eyes are large compared with those of most mammals. All birds need binocular vision ahead so that they can judge distances, since without it they would be unable to fly and land safely. For predatory birds such as owls, binocular vision is also vital for catching prey. By contrast, birds which are hunted need good all-round vision so that they can instantly spot danger approaching from any direction. An excellent example is the woodcock, which probes for its food with its beak and so does not greatly need binocular vision but can spot a predator approaching from any direction.

With all these adaptations, birds have evolved to be by far the fastest living creatures on the earth. The one disadvantage of specialising in flying is that birds have had to stay small in size or, like the example of the ostrich, give up flying altogether.

A diagram of a bird showing the internal organs. The complex digestive system and crop allows the bird to swallow its food rapidly, leaving the gizzard to break it down at a later stage.

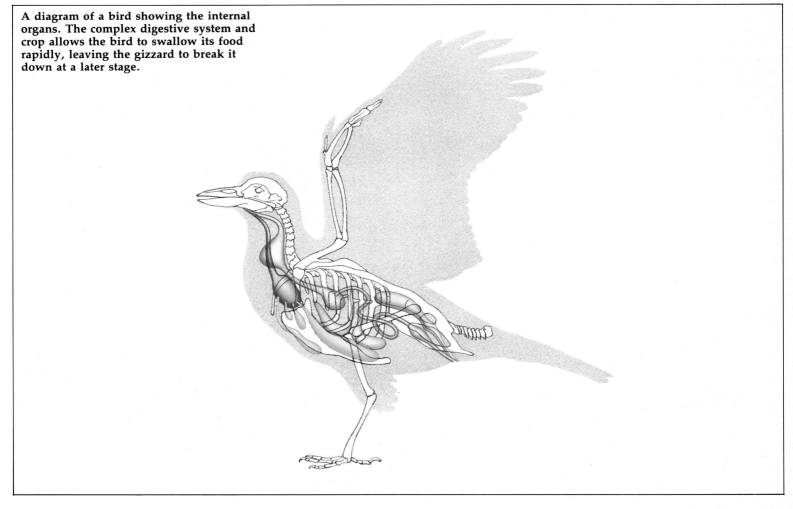

Migration

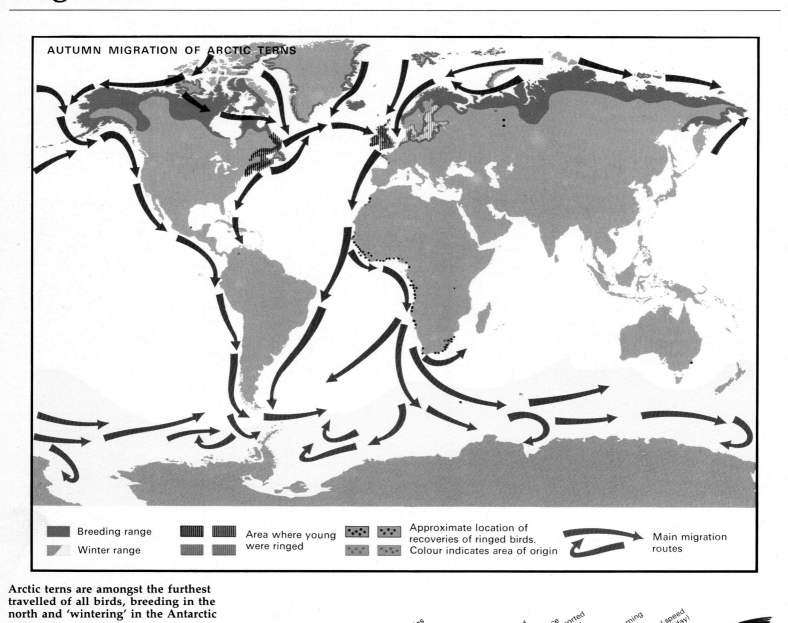

AUTUMN MIGRATION OF ARCTIC TERNS

▮ Breeding range	▦ ▦ Area where young were ringed	▦ ▦ Approximate location of recoveries of ringed birds.
▨ Winter range	▦ ▦	▦ ▦ Colour indicates area of origin

Main migration routes

Arctic terns are amongst the furthest travelled of all birds, breeding in the north and 'wintering' in the Antarctic summer.

Right: **Experiments with birds transported away from their nests confirm their ability to return swiftly over unfamiliar terrain.**

species	birds tested	distance transported (miles)	% returning	typical speed (miles/day)
Leach's Petrel	61	135-470	67	30
Manx Shearwater	42	265-415	90	200
Laysan Albatross	11	1665-4120	82	100
Gannet	18	213	63	100
Herring Gull	109	214-872	90	60
Common Tern	44	228-404	43	125
Swallow	21	240-310	52	150
Starling	68	200-440	46	25

Over most of the world, living conditions for birds change with the seasons. In much of the northern hemisphere, for example, winter may bring freezing cold and severe food shortages. In grasslands rainfall is often the key factor, food becoming increasingly scarce as the dry season progresses. With the power to travel rapidly over long distances birds can migrate into an area to enjoy its best season and rear their young, and leave before conditions become unsuitable again. But to do this they must be able to build up reserves of fuel, to find their way over long distances and to know the right time to set out on their journeys.

It seems that the urge to migrate is triggered by changes in the length of the days in spring and autumn. Some species then feed voraciously, doubling their weight with fat which will fuel their flight. The North American golden plover fattens up on berries in autumn and then undertakes a non-stop journey of 2400 miles down the western Atlantic from Labrador to South America. In this epic 48-hour flight it burns off about a third of its total body weight.

Some large birds (notably eagles, buzzards and storks) cannot travel far over water, because they are too heavy to fly long distances by flapping without becoming exhausted. Instead, to save energy, they glide long distances by the use of rising currents of warm air and updraughts caused by uneven ground. Such upcurrents never occur over the sea so these birds must avoid long journeys across water: great numbers may be seen on migration at places such as the Bosphorus, where they are funnelled between the Mediterranean and the Black Sea en route from eastern Europe to Africa.

Migration need not cover great distances. Some mountain birds simply go up or downhill with the changing seasons. On the other hand, many seabirds and waders undertake prodigious journeys. Arctic terns travel practically from one end of the earth to the other, living all the year in perpetual summer.

How long-distance travellers find their way is still not fully understood. Experiments show that some species can recognise constellations of stars and will fly towards them: others evidently use the sun and some use both. To navigate in this way means that birds must have an accurate sense of time so as to correct their courses as stars and sun move across the sky. However, this may not be the whole story. It appears that the earth's magnetic field may be detectable by certain species, so that they have a kind of built-in compass they can use when cloud obscures the heavens. Once they get close to their destinations, birds can certainly recognise local landmarks as is shown by the ability of swallows and martins to return year after year to the very same nest sites.

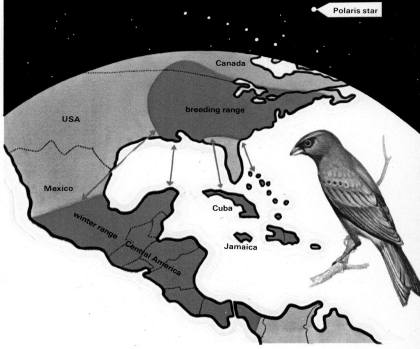

Above: **Cranes migrate by day, using the position of the sun to guide them.**

Top: **The Bosphorus is an important land bridge used by birds of prey and storks migrating from Europe to Africa. Here, a large flock of storks circles over Istanbul.**

Above: **Many species, such as the indigo bunting are nocturnal migrants: experiments show that they recognise constellations and use them for guidance.**

Courtship and territory

For most wild birds, the day-to-day problem of staying alive is no easy matter. Even finding the next meal can be a life and death affair, given the added hazards of bad weather and predators themselves searching for food. If a species is not to become extinct, each breeding season the survivors must produce enough young to make good the heavy toll of mortality.

Breeding is timed to coincide with the season when food is most abundant. In parts of the world where summer is short, birds may have to start courtship while conditions are still bad in order to have good conditions when the young hatch.

Males compete with each other to gain mates. Usually, their first step is to don breeding plumage that will attract females, intimidate other males and stand up to a summer's hard work. In many species, the next stage is to establish sole possession of a suitable territory containing a good choice of nest sites and enough food resources for the expected family.

Woodland birds usually sing to advertise their ownership of territory but those which live in open country, where they can easily be seen, often have a special display flight instead. If another male appears in an occupied territory it may challenge the owner. Then, the two males threaten each other with display or song. Fights are almost unknown, for the practical reason that neither bird can afford to risk getting injured: in the wild, injury generally means death. Usually the newcomer breaks down and leaves: prior occupancy of a territory gives the first male a great psychological advantage.

If a female appears, the male's first instinct will be to chase her off too, but her response will be a special display designed to show her peaceful intention.

Left: **Male ruffs display communally at a 'lek' and only dominant males mate with females.**

Right: **In many species, like the goldfinch, the male feeds his mate to help her gain condition for egg-laying.**

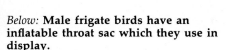

Below: **Male frigate birds have an inflatable throat sac which they use in display.**

Gradually, the male's aggression will turn to courtship, bringing both birds to the right state for mating. Usually at this stage, the male brings food to the female, helping her to gain the energy reserves she needs to make eggs. Meanwhile the hen selects a nest site and building commences. Soon, the pair will copulate, the male fertilising the developing eggs which will be ready to lay once the nest is finished.

There are many exceptions to this general pattern. For example, in a few species the males do not establish territories but meet in groups to display communally. Females visit these 'leks' and are fertilised by the dominant males. This is the only contact between the sexes, the jobs of nestbuilding, incubation and care of the young falling to the females alone.

Above left: **Black-headed gulls mating.**

Above right: **While males are often brightly plumaged, females are generally camouflaged. Here a pair of coucal are seen at their nest.**

Right: **Snipe display in flight, extended tail feathers making a loud 'bleating' noise when they dive.**

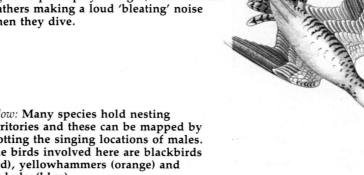

Below: **Many species hold nesting territories and these can be mapped by plotting the singing locations of males. The birds involved here are blackbirds (red), yellowhammers (orange) and skylarks (blue).**

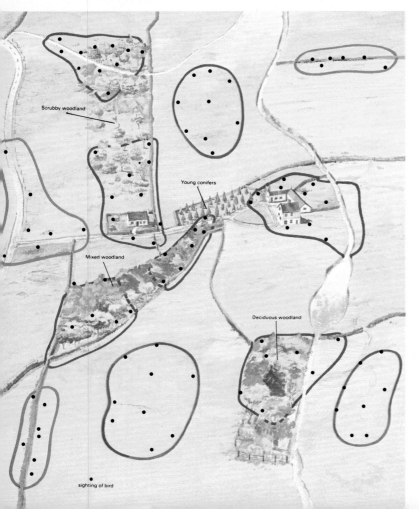

Ring ouzel cock singing from a conspicuous perch.

Nests and eggs

It takes about three days for an egg to form within a female bird and during that period it must be fertilised by the male. Once egg laying begins, it usually continues at daily intervals until the clutch is complete. Generally, incubation does not start until this stage, so that the young hatch and leave the nest together. However, many birds of prey start incubation with the first egg: this means that the chicks hatch in sequence over a period of days and, if a food shortage arises, at least the older, larger chicks have a chance to survive by taking all the available food. In any event, once the incubation process begins it must continue without a break until the eggs hatch. The developing embryos cannot stand prolonged chilling, although brief absence by a parent will do no harm.

As feathers are very good insulation, they retain body heat very efficiently. But when incubating her eggs the hen wishes to transfer her body heat to them. Consequently she moults the downy feathers of her lower breast and retains only the thin outer coat of contour feathers. Some species actually pluck out their own down to line and insulate their nests.

Throughout this period the incubating birds and especially the eggs are at great risk from predators. For this reason, most birds seek to conceal their nests in dense vegetation or within cavities in trees or rocks. Camouflage is most important to ground nesters and there is a tendency for females to have inconspicuous plumage wherever they nest, because they are usually responsible for incubation, while males continue with defence of the territory for which they need eye-catching and, to their rivals, intimidating coloration.

Some species rely for safety mainly on inaccessibility. Thus, weavers construct incredibly complicated globes suspended from the ends of thin branches, that are easy to see but hard to reach. Eagles select trees or crags and, if the site proves safe, they will return to it year after year,

Above right: **Eider ducks line their nests with copious soft down which helps to keep the eggs warm in sub-arctic conditions.**

Right: **The fairy tern, breeding in the still, warm airs of tropical Pacific islands, builds no nest at all but simply balances its single egg on a bare branch.**

Opposite top: **Large birds of prey, like these African fish eagles, construct huge, conspicuous nests, relying partly on inaccessibility and partly on their own size to give them protection.**

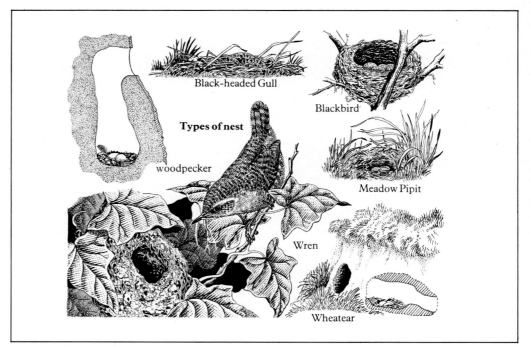

Types of nest

Black-headed Gull

Blackbird

woodpecker

Meadow Pipit

Wren

Wheatear

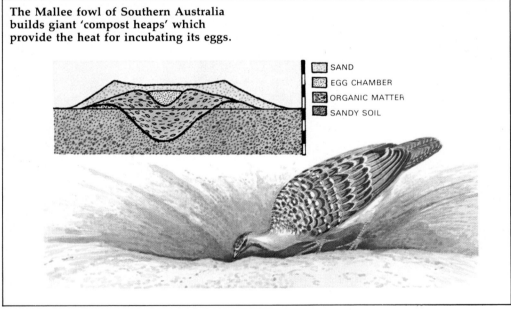

The Mallee fowl of Southern Australia builds giant 'compost heaps' which provide the heat for incubating its eggs.

SAND
EGG CHAMBER
ORGANIC MATTER
SANDY SOIL

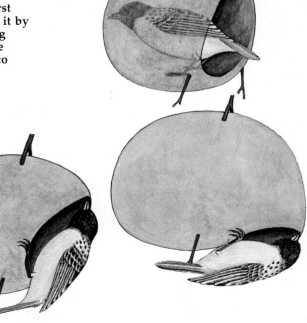

adding new material until it becomes quite huge – the largest known was reputedly 5·4 metres high and well over 1·8 metres wide.

Uniquely, the brush turkey of Australasia build special mounds of vegetation covered by sand in which the eggs are incubated by the heat of decomposing vegetation. These mounds may be as much as ten metres across with some species. The male bird visits the mound daily and tests its temperature with his beak, adding or removing material in order to adjust the heat. Incubation can take as long as nine weeks and throughout that period the male labours constantly, shifting material to and fro. Once young brush turkeys hatch, they dig themselves out and set off on their own into the wide world. They are an exception. Other young birds can expect careful parental care before they have to make their own way in life.

Right: **The African village weaver constructs a nest of palm fibres, first forming a ring and then enlarging it by stages. Suspended from a drooping branch, and with the entrance hole beneath, it is largely inaccessible to predators.**

19

Young birds

The young of birds which nest in relative safety off the ground, hatch naked, blind and helpless: their parents carry food to them not only until they can flutter away from the nest but also thereafter for several days for most small birds and for weeks with some large ones.

Ground-nesting birds are very vulnerable to predators. The chicks of wildfowl, waders and most other similar species hatch clothed in warm, camouflaged down and are able to feed themselves. As soon as possible, they are led away from the nest by the adults, whose job it is to provide shelter at night and in rain by brooding the young, and to provide warning of danger, when the chicks will crouch motionless while their parents attempt to drive or draw the predator away. By contrast, birds which nest on the ground in large colonies, such as gulls and terns, often have enough mass 'air power' to be able to attack and drive off marauders, so the young do not need to leave the nest until they are well grown.

The time it takes to care for the young until they become independent limits the number of offspring which can be produced each year. A handful of birds, including cuckoos in Europe, cowbirds in America and wydahs in Africa, evade this constraint by laying their eggs in other species' nests. Thus, they can concentrate all their energies on egg production and produce more young than if they had to rear the chicks themselves.

All these different systems of rearing young have the same purpose – ensuring the survival of the species. The majority of young birds die in their first winter before they have become experienced. As they grow older, so their chances of survival increase but, even so, few small birds live beyond the age of three. Such species have to produce large numbers of young: for instance, under good conditions one pair of European great tits may raise two broods, amounting to about 20 chicks, in one season. At the other extreme, many larger birds are very long lived once they reach maturity. They may not begin to breed until they

The young of ground-nesting birds can feed themselves from birth (precocial), but birds which nest in safer situations have chicks which are helpless when they hatch (altricial).

Blackbird nestling
(altricial) – 3 days old

Lapwing chick
(precocial) – 3 days old

are about four years old or more and then perhaps rear one chick a year for 20 years.

In practice, there are many breeding failures. The great tits might lose all their young to a marauding weasel, or have them drowned in the nest hole by torrential rain, so that the exceptionally good years when 20 young leave the nest, are balanced by others when none are produced. Large birds too have breeding failures due to predators, bad weather or accident. But these individual tragedies do not matter to the species provided that, by the end of its life, each adult has produced just one survivor to replace it in the breeding population.

Opposite: **The Australian striped honeyeater raises three or four chicks in the safety of a purse-shaped nest suspended near the end of a drooping branch.**

Goshawks *(below)* **have small broods, cared for by both parents, so that the survival rate is high. Mallard ducks** *(bottom)* **have large broods, cared for by the female alone, so that the survival rate is low. The number of young surviving at the start of the first winter is probably similar in both species.**

Above: **Young great black-backed gull in second winter plumage (top) and juvenile. By their fourth winter, they will be white with black wings and backs. The following summer, those which have survived will breed.**

Below: **Young cuckoo being fed by a reed warbler.**

Extinction and conservation

Birds, like, all other living creatures, live in a competitive world. Individuals within a species compete for food and for mates and those best suited to the demands of their environment survive to breed successfully. Different species also tend to compete with each other where the requirements for food or nesting habitat overlap.

Head-on competition may be fatal for the losers, and so instead species avoid this by becoming more specialised – exploiting their environment in different ways. At the same time, healthy species are constantly trying to expand, producing more young than needed to replace normal adult mortality. This surplus enables them quickly to take advantage of any increase in available food resources, resulting either from the decline of a near competitor or from some external circumstances affecting the habitat on which they depend.

Because natural conditions are never static there is always an ebb and flow in the affairs of species. In the long-term whole continents split and re-form; mountains erode and new peaks arise elsewhere; climate changes.

Relatively quickly, forest may replace grassland or a lake silt up and become a reedbed. The effect on species depends on both the extent and the rate of change. If conditions change gradually over a long period, a species may be able to evolve with them. This is because each generation is made up of individuals with different qualities. Thus if, for example, the climate cools very slowly those individuals which are most cold tolerant will tend to survive better and

Birds of prey have suffered heavily in developed countries from deliberate human persecution and loss of habitat. A number are endangered including the Spanish imperial eagle *(below)* and the Californian condor *(right)*.

Akiapolaau
(extinct honeycreeper)

Moho nobilis
(extinct honeyeater)

Palila
(honeycreeper)

Once occurring in immense flocks in North America, Eskimo curlew were killed in great numbers for sport and food in the last century. Only a handful exist today.

Without doubt, in the course of avian history a huge number of bird species have become extinct naturally from both causes. Now man is the main cause of terminal extinction. Some birds have been exterminated by over-exploitation for food. More have been wiped out as a result of the introduction of alien predators against which they have no defence. The greatest losses have been due to the destruction of habitat: the felling of forests, the drainage of wetlands, the ploughing of the prairies. Only in the last few decades have we begun to seek the conservation of endangered species, and it will need major changes in land use policy worldwide if the hundreds of different species now at risk are to be saved.

contribute most young to the next generation. It in turn will contain some individuals even more cold-tolerant than their parents. Slowly, over many generations – perhaps hundreds or thousands of years – the species will change its character, adapting itself to a changing environment until perhaps it no longer remotely resembles its original ancestors. This is known as evolutionary extinction.

If change is rapid, then a species may be unable to respond to it quickly enough. A rapid cooling of climate could outstrip the ability of a species to withstand the cold, and all its members would die. This is known as terminal extinction.

Many Hawaiian species became extinct partly as a result of habitat destruction and partly through competition from alien bird species introduced by man.

A flightless seabird, the great auk was exploited by mariners as a source of fresh meat and huge numbers were boiled down to produce lamp oil. The last individual was killed in 1844.

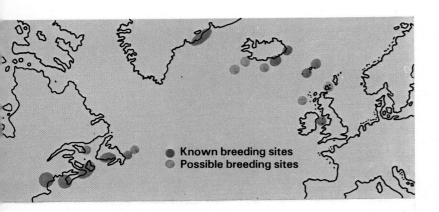

Known breeding sites
Possible breeding sites

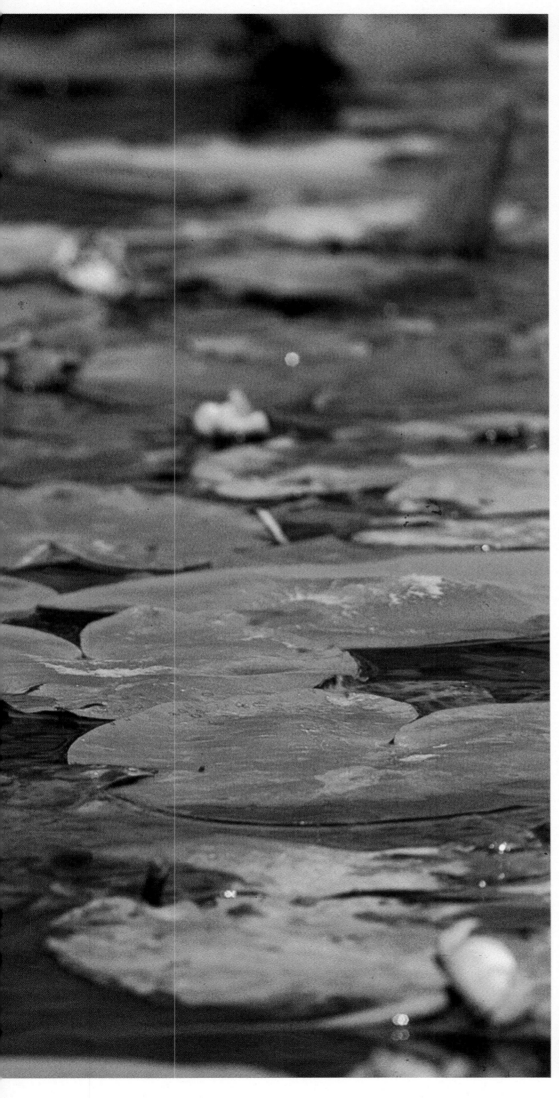

Bird Habitats of the World

The first problem that faces all creatures is how to stay alive. All living things at all times are under the pressures put on them by the habitats in which they live and by the other creatures with which they compete. Birds have been in the past, and remain, a very successful group of creatures in exploiting the world's habitats. They occupy an enormous variety of environments. Thus some drink nectar in the constant summer of the tropical forests while others incubate their eggs in the continuous darkness and horrifying cold of an Antarctic mid-winter: some soar without apparent effort in the thin high air above mountain peaks but others pursue their prey for long minutes deep beneath the cold water of the oceans.

The ability to migrate has enabled birds to exploit habitats that provide suitable food sources for only part of the year. Indeed, some species will occupy several different habitats in a single year.

To see how birds relate to their environment and to each other within them, the following pages describe the major habitat types of the world and some of the main bird families that are found within them.

Coot with a chick riding on its back amongst yellow water lillies in a secluded pond in western Europe. Coot have evolved partially webbed feet which enable them not only to swim and dive but also to move about freely on land.

Tundra

The tundra is a vast and treeless habitat stretching across the north of America, Europe and Asia that presents birds with enormous challenges and great opportunities. In winter, snow covers the frozen ground and the days are very short. In summer, there is almost constant daylight, the soil surface becomes marshy and sprinkled with thousands of pools. There is a rich growth of ground vegetation, insects become abundant and small mammals such as lemmings breed rapidly: the potential food supply is, briefly, generous.

Because the winter conditions are so severe, few creatures can live here throughout the year. This gives an advantage to migratory birds because they can move into the habitat to exploit its riches during the short summer with little competition. Wildfowl and waders in particular find it ideal.

The tundra breeding season is brief and no time must be wasted. Many wildfowl complete their courtship in their wintering areas so that nest construction and egg laying can begin quickly when the birds reach their breeding grounds.

Left: **Snowy owls are one of the few bird species able to live on the tundra for all of the year. Their insulating plumage gives them good protection against extreme cold.**

Most tundra birds are summer visitors including the bean goose *(top right)* **and long-tailed duck, known as the old squaw in North America** *(bottom right).* **The snow bunting** *(centre right)* **is one of the few small birds to occur: generally, they find it harder to resist cold conditions than do larger species.**

The demands of migration may be considerable; on arrival, birds must concentrate on feeding busily to regain condition – particularly the females, which have to produce the eggs. With red-necked phalaropes, incubation and care of the young is entirely the responsibility of the males: presumably after the females have migrated from the equatorial oceans where they winter, and then produced eggs, they are incapable of undergoing the prolonged semi-starvation of the incubation period.

Snowy owl populations fluctuate greatly with the fortunes of the lemmings on which they largely prey. When these are abundant the owls rear large broods – more than the habitat can possibly sup-

Below: **Many tundra species, like the red-necked phalarope, have very widespread distributions throughout the circumpolar habitat. Unusually, it is the male that incubates the nest as shown below.**

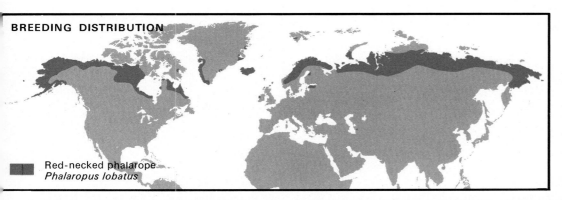

BREEDING DISTRIBUTION

■ Red-necked phalarope
Phalaropus lobatus

Above: **a gyrfalcon stooping at a ptarmigan. Both species live in the tundra throughout the year**

port in winter. Then, many of the birds are obliged to move south, well outside their normal range. Such occasional 'irruptions' are a feature of the lives of many tundra and boreal forest residents.

Tundra is not exclusive to the far north, but occurs on a small scale at the tip of South America and at high altitudes on mountains elsewhere.

The Northern forests

South of the tundra, mean temperatures are generally warmer, the summer is a little longer and the winter gales less fierce. Here, trees can begin to survive – scattered and stunted willows and spruce on the fringes of the open tundra lands giving way to taller timber and finally to dense coniferous forest.

Because the northern forest varies little from one area to another, a number of bird species or closely-related groups are distributed throughout the entire 8000 mile extent of the zone across Europe,

Asia and America. For example, because there are coniferous trees throughout these forests, all three continents contain crossbills, which feed by prising up the scales of cones with their crossed mandibles to get at the tiny, nutritious seeds within. Different crossbill species have evolved different-sized beaks suitable for different sorts of cones. Thus, the crossbill group can exploit the seeds of many different types of conifer, and competition between the different species is minimised.

Crossbills must breed to take advantage of the time when cones are ripe and opening naturally, making seeds easy to gather. As this often occurs in mid-winter, the young birds must be able to tolerate temperatures far below freezing. Where most naked nestlings would die in minutes, young crossbills merely become torpid while their parents are away from the nest collecting food: when the adults return to brood them, they quickly recover and feed.

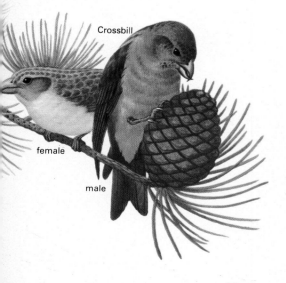

Crossbill
female
male

Left: **Crossbills are adapted to feeding on conifer seeds grasping the cones with strong feet while they prise the scales open with their beaks.**

Right: **Great grey owls occur throughout the northern forests of all three continents, feeding on small and medium sized mammals.**

Above: **Feeding on insects and fruit, waxwings have no regular winter migration pattern but merely move as far south as is necessary to find adequate supplies of food.**

Right: **Coniferous forest habitats occur in many mountain ranges south of the true northern forests. Stellar's jay occurs in such forests along the length of the Rockies as far south as Panama.**

Insects become plentiful in the forest in summer, when many small warblers migrate into the habitat to breed, but in winter few insectivorous species remain. Those that do stay commonly form mixed flocks and seek food together. This habit may give them increased protection from birds of prey, because a flock is little easier to find in a forest than a single bird but it has many more watchful eyes, so its members can each spend more time looking for food and less watching for danger than if they searched separately.

As an insurance against the inevitable shortage of food in winter, many titmice or chickadees habitually store surplus food during the summer, tucking insects, spiders and seeds away in crevices where they may chance upon them while searching through the trees in winter. There is no evidence that titmice actually remember where they have hidden individual food items but it is certainly the case that some other forest residents which cache food do know just where they have put it. Nutcrackers can find their food stores even under snow.

Collaboration and foresight are usually considered to be amongst the special qualities of mankind. But birds evolved these abilities long before man, and, using them, can survive under conditions which even he finds almost intolerable.

The thick-billed nutcracker stores food in autumn for use during winter and early springtime shortages.

Game birds

Western man has given the general title of game birds to two related groups which have the misfortune to taste good. One group is the Tetraonidae: the grouse family; the other is the Phasianidae: the partridges, quails and pheasants.

There are 17 different species of grouse in the world, all living in northern habitats – grasslands, forests and tundra – and most of them in North America. They are primarily vegetarians eating shoots, buds, seeds and berries. The majority are exclusively ground dwellers but the woodland grouse species do venture into the trees to feed. Grouse prefer to walk or run rather than fly. Their reaction to the approach of large birds of prey such as the golden eagle or peregrine fal-

Right: **two common gamebirds, the pheasant** *(above)* **and the partridge** *(below).* **The pheasant's long tail allows it maximum manoeuvrability in its woodland habitat.**

Left: **British red grouse have no special winter plumage but European grouse and ptarmigan moult into pure white for winter.**

con is to crouch and hide but if forced to take to the air by danger on the ground, their stubby, rounded wings give them a good sprint capability over short distances.

Most species have communal mating displays. The males meet at traditional 'leks' where they display to each other, dominant birds winning central places and mating with most of the females, who are solely responsible for nest building, incubation and care of the young. While the females of these species have camouflaged plumage, the males are usually strikingly coloured, with extra

Below: **Many grouse, like these north American prairie chickens, are lekking species. Here, two cocks are displaying before a hen.**

adornments such as plumes or inflatable throat sacs. In monogamous species, where males assist in rearing the young, both sexes have plumages which blend in with their habitats. The finest example of this is the ptarmigan – a tundra resident – which is a beautiful mottled brown in summer and moults into pure white in winter when the snows come.

Partridge and quail, like grouse, are plump ground dwellers and mostly reluctant to fly, though the Eurasian quail is a long-distance migrant which winters in the Sahara. They tend to inhabit warmer habitats than grouse, from grassland through to near desert. There are over 80 species of quail and partridge in the Old World and 36 species of New World quail. All are monogamous, both adults caring for the young and in most species large family parties remain together throughout the winter, only breaking up when spring comes.

The pheasants are Asiatic in origin. There are nearly 50 species, most of which inhabit high altitude forests though some such as the peacock and the jungle fowl (the ancestor of the domestic chicken) are tropical forest birds. Only the Congo pheasant is found in Africa. The original distribution of some species has been greatly altered through widespread introductions by man, mainly for sport shooting but partly because many of the males are strikingly handsome birds. Outside the breeding season, pheasants tend to be solitary but in spring each male seeks to collect a harem of several females with which to mate, although it takes no parental responsibilities.

The mottled plumage of a hen ptarmigan gives her superb camouflage in the tundra.

Taking no part in the care of young, male ruffed grouse (below) **can devote all their energies to elaborate plumage and display.**

Because of their brilliant plumages, many pheasant species have been introduced by man into countries all over the world. These are Swinhoe's pheasant, (left) **golden pheasant** (top right) **and Lady Amhurst's pheasant** (bottom).

Temperate woodlands

In the temperate zones of the world, woodlands occur wherever there is adequate rainfall. In any such wood there are many different tree species and a wide variety of ground vegetation, shrubs and flowering plants, which in turn support innumerable insects, small mammals and other creatures. This means that there are an enormous number of different ways for birds to exploit the habitat, each species occupying a particular 'niche' for feeding or breeding which minimises competition.

For example, in summer a wood in Europe is full of insect-eating birds, including some which are normally seed-eaters but rear their young on insects. A num-

ber, such as the wood warbler, feed only in the canopy, fluttering amongst the topmost leaves. Blue tits are particularly agile, hanging head downwards to pry into bunches of foliage that even wood warblers find hard to reach. Amongst the stouter twigs and branches, larger birds such as the chaffinch move more sedately, perhaps stretching for a choice caterpillar but rarely getting off balance. By contrast, the treecreeper never ventures into the canopy at all, but instead runs mouselike up the trunk and main branches to pry into cavities with a long, curved bill. Other species, like the garden warbler, feed mostly in the understorey of bushes and young trees. Wrens

The American robin is widespread in both boreal and temperate woodlands of North America.

forage even closer to the ground amongst the herbage and fallen boughs while robins prefer to seek food on the ground itself amongst the litter of dead leaves. Spotted flycatchers take most of their food on the wing, flitting out from their perches to snap up passing flies.

Competition for nest sites is similarly reduced by different preferences. The chaffinch lodges its nest at the fork of a branch, the garden warbler low down in dense shrubbery, wood warblers on the ground itself. Blue tits prefer holes in trees, ideally one with a tiny entrance which only they can squeeze through. Treecreepers look for sites behind loose bark. Flycatchers will nest in much more open cavities, perhaps where a bough has torn off, while the wren might site its mossy nest in the rotting end of the fallen bough itself. Robins particularly like holes or places behind ivy.

Because the habitat is so varied, it can support many more species in summer than northern forests do. However, though winter cold is less severe in temperate woods, food does become scarce which means that many insectivorous species must migrate south in autumn. Whether migrant or resident, many of these birds – especially the young inexperienced ones – will die before the following spring when the survivors come to breed again in the greenwood.

Green Woodpecker

Coal Tit

Great Spotted
Woodpecker

Nuthatch

Woodcock

Above: **As one adult wood warbler brings food, the other removes a chick's dropping from the nest**

Left: **The wood is like a multi-storey hotel with different species feeding in different 'niches' to minimise competition.**

Below: **Most garden birds – like the starling** *(left),* **blue tit** *(top)* **and great tit** *(bottom)* **are woodland species. However, the house sparrow** *(right)* **is adapted to arid habitats, which is why it is so successful in towns.**

Woodpeckers

The woodpecker's tongue is especially elastic and can reach up to four times the length of its beak, probing holes for insect grubs and other food.

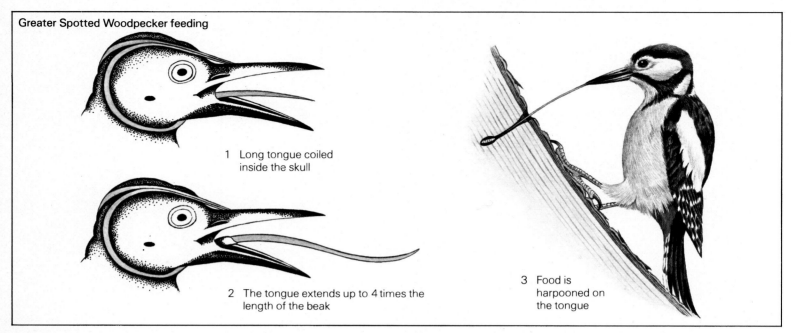

Greater Spotted Woodpecker feeding

1 Long tongue coiled inside the skull

2 The tongue extends up to 4 times the length of the beak

3 Food is harpooned on the tongue

Woodpeckers have developed a range of adaptions which enable them to exploit a niche largely unavilable to other birds – the trunks and undersides of the branches of trees. This has enabled them to spread widely throughout the world, though they have not yet colonised Australasia and Madagascar. There are about 200 species of which the vast majority are true woodpeckers. Two are the wrynecks, which are regarded as 'primitive' species that do not have woodpecking adaptations, and eight are the tiny piculets which have characteristics intermediate between the other two groups.

All true woodpeckers have a similar basic structure. Their chisel beaks can cut into wood and are mounted on a skull which is especially constructed to withstand the stresses of hammering, while the whole unit is powered by strong muscles. To provide a firm working platform, a woodpecker hangs on the trunk of the tree, sharp claws gripping the bark (with two toes forward and two back), and props itself on its tail (the centre shafts of the feathers being strong enough to support it). From this position it can hammer powerfully to break into the galleries of wood-boring insects. The woodpecker's tongue is mounted on a structure of elastic tissue and flexible bone which passes in two strips around the back of the bird's skull and over the

A male Williamson's sapsucker, a species of the North American pine woods.

The acorn woodpecker of the United States stores acorns by inserting them into holes bored into trees.

Below: The cock red-bellied woodpecker taps inside the nest hole to encourage the mate; she alights outside and taps out her answer.

The yellow-naped woodpecker *(top)* **is structurally a true woodpecker but the African piculet** *(above)* **is less specialised, lacking the strengthened tail.**

top of the head, and is anchored at the right nostril. This produces a spring-like device, enabling the bird to probe with its tongue along insect galleries for up to four times the length of its beak – (13cm or more depending on the species). Backward-pointing barbs at its tip harpoon the prey and pull it out as the tongue springs back.

One group of North American woodpeckers, the sapsuckers, specialises in feeding on the sap which exudes from the holes that it drills. Other species, including the European green woodpecker, feed mainly on the ground, and especially at ants nests where their long sticky tongues are ideal for probing the galleries. In winter, when the ants retreat underground, green woodpeckers will break down the nests to reach them.

As well as insects, many species take tree seeds such as acorns and cones, wedging them into clefts or crannies so that they can be hammered open. The North American acorn woodpecker deliberately excavates little cavities in which to store its favourite food for use during times of shortage.

Woodpeckers use their wood-boring skill to excavate nesting holes and, incidentally, provide a useful service to other hole nesting birds which will use these sites in subsequent years.

Some species use their hammering as a form of song. Selection of a resonating branch ensures that their 'drumming' is amplified and carries over long distances.

Above: **The wryneck is a 'primitive' woodpecker, nesting in natural cavities and feeding largely on ants.**

Below: **The red-shafted flicker is a true woodpecker which feeds mainly on the ground, particularly on ants.**

Owls

When darkness falls, most birds are already at their roosts, sheltering from predators, wind and rain. Owls, on the other hand, are wakeful. Stretching wings and legs after a day of inactivity, they prepare for the night's hunting. The largest of them, the eagle owls, stand 76cm tall and have a 1·5m wingspan: they may tackle and kill creatures a good deal larger than themselves including foxes, jackals, young roe deer and other birds of prey. The smallest is the elf owl, a 15cm tall insect hunter. Between the two extremes there are about 130 other kinds of owl, preying on mammals, birds, fish and crustaceans, worms and insects – in fact, owls take every sort of live prey, hunt in every type of habitat and have colonised every continent except Antarctica.

Nocturnal activity demands special powers of sight and hearing. It has been suggested that an owl's eyesight is up to 100 times as light sensitive as man's. During daylight, they protect their eyes from damage by expanding the coloured iris and closing the pupil. Even the most nocturnal of them can move about by day if disturbed, while most species hunt regularly in the half light of dawn and dusk, and a few have become wholly diurnal.

An owl's hearing is exceedingly acute. The ear openings are located on the sides of the face, sometimes forming a semicircle reaching from above each eye to below it. Concealed within the 'facial

Below: **The brown fish owl is one of five Asiatic and African species which regularly enter water to capture fish, frogs and crustaceans. Their legs are not feathered, unlike those of other owls.**

Great Eagle Owl

Elf Owl

The largest of the owls, the eagle owl, which can attack deer, perched next to the smallest, the elf owl, which mainly eats invertebrates.

disc' of flattened feathers, which may itself act like a radar disc to catch faint sounds, the ears are fitted with movable flaps to help sound location. In many species the ear aperture on one side of the face is higher than on the other. This gives owls great accuracy in judging the location of sounds rising from below them – the usual location of prey.

The 'ear tufts' have nothing to do with hearing. Varying subtly from species to species in their particular size and location, they create a distinctive head silhouette. Meeting in the dark, quick identification at a safe distance is important when the other bird could be your mate, a potential competitor for living space or even an enemy capable of killing you.

Small birds recognise all owls as dangerous. If they find one at roost by day, they will gather round and mob it by calling loudly. The effect is to ensure that no bird in the neighbourhood is unaware of the potential danger that threatens them all by night.

Opposite: **The North American screech owl will take any kind of prey small enough to overpower. In the split second before capture, the wings are spread and pushed forward to brake the bird's momentum, its eyes focus precisely on the prey and the feet – themselves sound-muffled by furry feathers – are extended. Owls can swivel one toe around, changing the three-forward and one-back arrangement best for perching to a two-forward and two-back grasp ideal for killing prey by squeezing with the feet and driving in the dagger-like talons. As shown by the examples below.**

Brown Fish Owl

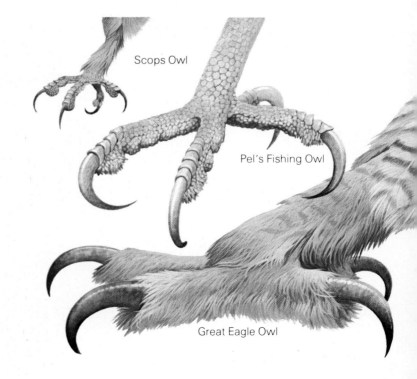

Scops Owl

Pel's Fishing Owl

Great Eagle Owl

SILENT FLIGHT

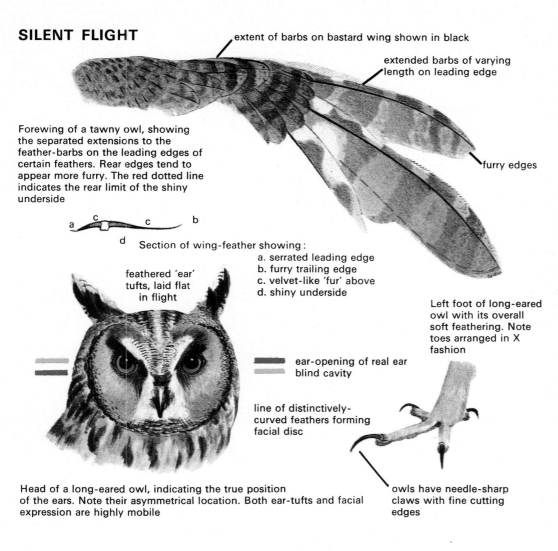

extent of barbs on bastard wing shown in black

extended barbs of varying length on leading edge

furry edges

Forewing of a tawny owl, showing the separated extensions to the feather-barbs on the leading edges of certain feathers. Rear edges tend to appear more furry. The red dotted line indicates the rear limit of the shiny underside

Section of wing-feather showing:
a. serrated leading edge
b. furry trailing edge
c. velvet-like 'fur' above
d. shiny underside

feathered 'ear' tufts, laid flat in flight

ear-opening of real ear
blind cavity

line of distinctively-curved feathers forming facial disc

Left foot of long-eared owl with its overall soft feathering. Note toes arranged in X fashion

Head of a long-eared owl, indicating the true position of the ears. Note their asymmetrical location. Both ear-tufts and facial expression are highly mobile

owls have needle-sharp claws with fine cutting edges

Owls need to fly silently, firstly to catch prey unawares and secondly to be able to hear without interference.

When handling an owl the most striking feature is the soft, velvety plumage. Many feathers, even the largest, are covered above with a fine velvet-like 'fur'. The body-feathers, including the under-wing lining, are particularly soft. The leading and trailing edges of some primaries have sound-deadening features (see illustration).

The faces of many owls are highly mobile so that the facial disc may change considerably in shape according to the mood of the bird. The true function of the disc and especially the layered curly feathers which form its edge is not known but possibly they reduce the rush of air past the large ears, which are hidden beneath the feathers. Notice that the bill is almost obscured by bristles and that the feet — extended at the vital moment of capture — are heavily sound-proofed. The undersides of the flight-feathers are shiny and smooth (the degree varying between species). The extent of this is shown by the red dotted line on the wing (left)

Tropical forests

Tropical forests grow where temperatures remain high throughout the year and there is generous rainfall, creating an extended and continuous growing season. This has three very important effects for birds. Firstly, the forests are incredibly diverse in character and, because of the great number of specialised 'niches' available, able to support a great diversity of birds. A count in Ecuador found 200 different species occurring in one 5 hectare plot. Secondly, in turn this means that no individual species can be particularly common in one place – a striking contrast with boreal forests where there are many fewer species, each with a very extensive distribution.

The third major effect of the continuous growing season and the constant availability of food is that there is no need for birds to be migrants – the forest is fully occupied year round by resident species.

Insects, fruit and nectar are the main food sources for the birds in these forests. Fruit grows mainly in the canopy where parrots, toucans, fruit pigeons and others feed on it, moving around from one part of the forest to another as different crops ripen. This soft food requires

Below:
Many tropical forest birds, such as the South American quetzal, have brightly coloured or bizarre plumages. Growing these absorbs a significant part of the bird's energy resources, which is probably why species in less stable habitats, and particularly migrants, cannot afford such elaborate ornamentation.

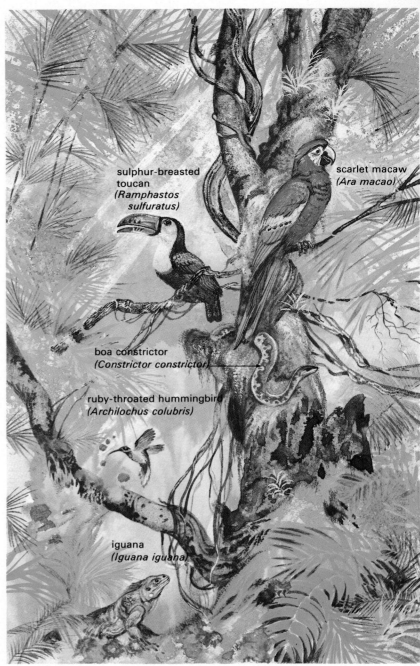

sulphur-breasted toucan
(*Ramphastos sulfuratus*)

scarlet macaw
(*Ara macao*)

boa constrictor
(*Constrictor constrictor*)

ruby-throated hummingbird
(*Archilochus colubris*)

iguana
(*Iguana iguana*)

Above: **Gloomy tropical forests contain well-lit areas in which brightly coloured fauna show up well.**

38

Canopy

Blue-grey Tanager

Black-necked Red Cotinga

Intermediate

Scythebill

Toucan Barbet

Forest floor

Tinamou

Streak chested Antpitta

Tropical forests are even more diverse than temperate woodlands providing 'niches' for a remarkable variety of birds which live at different levels in the forest.

no particular beak adaptations and birds with very different bills feed on it. However, it has been suggested that the large beaks of toucans enable these heavy birds to reach out for fruit growing on branches too slender to take their weight. Fruit pigeons have very wide gapes and can gulp down whole fruit up to 5cm across.

Birds, such as humming birds, which feed on nectar usually have specially adapted tongues, which are either long and grooved or brush-like, enabling them to suck or lap up the liquid without fouling their plumage.

With no major seasonal temperature change, breeding is usually synchronised with the wet season when forest productivity is at its highest. Clutch size in most tropical birds is only two eggs, comparing oddly with the much larger broods of birds of colder habitats. It is possible that, living sedentary lives in stable and rich habitats, tropical forest birds are longer lived than many other species, thus needing to produce fewer young to maintain their numbers.

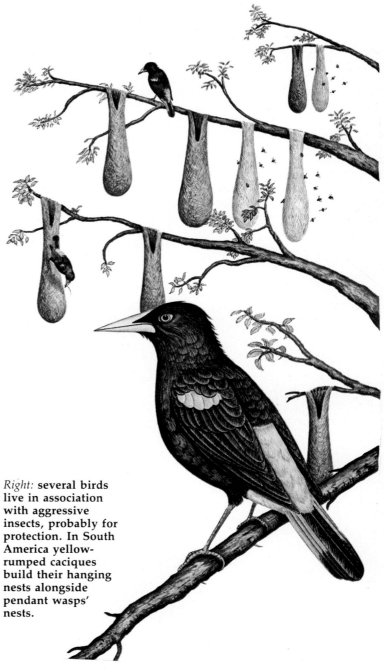

Below: **Birds flocking to a fruiting fig tree: (from left) bushy-crested hornbill, large green pigeon, cinnamon-headed green pigeon and Malay lorikeet.**

Right: **several birds live in association with aggressive insects, probably for protection. In South America yellow-rumped caciques build their hanging nests alongside pendant wasps' nests.**

Canopy

Blue-grey Tanager

Black-necked Red Cotinga

Intermediate

Scythebill

Toucan Barbet

Forest floor

Tinamou

Streak chested Antpitta

Below: **Birds flocking to a fruiting fig tree:** *(from left)* **bushy-crested hornbill, large green pigeon, cinnamon-headed green pigeon and Malay lorikeet.**

Tropical forests are even more diverse than temperate woodlands providing 'niches' for a remarkable variety of birds which live at different levels in the forest.

no particular beak adaptations and birds with very different bills feed on it. However, it has been suggested that the large beaks of toucans enable these heavy birds to reach out for fruit growing on branches too slender to take their weight. Fruit pigeons have very wide gapes and can gulp down whole fruit up to 5cm across.

Birds, such as humming birds, which feed on nectar usually have specially adapted tongues, which are either long and grooved or brush-like, enabling them to suck or lap up the liquid without fouling their plumage.

With no major seasonal temperature change, breeding is usually synchronised with the wet season when forest productivity is at its highest. Clutch size in most tropical birds is only two eggs, comparing oddly with the much larger broods of birds of colder habitats. It is possible that, living sedentary lives in stable and rich habitats, tropical forest birds are longer lived than many other species, thus needing to produce fewer young to maintain their numbers.

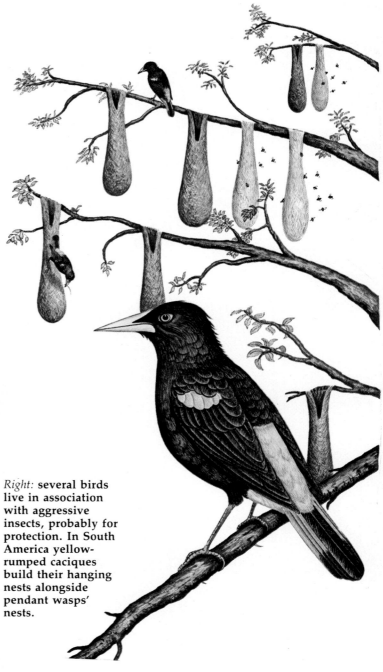

Right: **several birds live in association with aggressive insects, probably for protection. In South America yellow-rumped caciques build their hanging nests alongside pendant wasps' nests.**

Parrots

Parrots are found in tropical and subtropical forests all over the world. Some species have colonised savannahs and grasslands, and a few occur in temperature habitats, several Australian species surviving even where winter snow occurs.

In total there are about 330 species variously known as parrots, parakeets, macaws and lovebirds. All have hooked powerful beaks, suited to feeding on hard-shelled seeds and nuts which are held against the curve of the upper mandible and husked or cracked by pressure from the lower one. However, the family is also fond of fruit and some species have evolved brush-like structures on their tongues to feed on pollen or nectar. Many species also take insects.

Their feet, like those of woodpeckers, have two toes pointing forwards and two backwards, giving them a very strong grasp. Using their beaks like a third foot, they are agile if careful climbers and well able to reach food hanging at the tips of swaying boughs. Some species also have the habit, unique amongst birds, of picking up food in one foot to eat it – an important skill for dealing with awkward items like large fruit or nuts in the swaying treetops.

However, not all species are tree-living; some spend most of their time on the ground, picking up the seeds of shrubs and grasses, while two species are almost flightless.

Most parrots are monogamous and pair for life. Even though they spend most of their time in family groups or large flocks, pairs remain close together all year round and will often sit side by side, preening each other when not feeding.

Nests are made in holes, but few species actually originate their own sites: most simply enlarge a natural cavity or an old woodpecker hole. Some, such as the Patagonian conure, dig burrows in the ground or under rocks. The American monk parrot is exceptional, gathering twigs and branches to build a huge communal nest in a tree, each pair of birds having its own apartment in the structure.

At first when the young hatch, the female remains with them almost constantly, relying on the male to bring food to her with which in turn she feeds the young. Birds which rear their young on insects deliver them whole by the beakful, but seed-eaters which rear their young on the same diet, as do parrots, swallow the food and partially digest it before regurgitating it into their chicks' beaks. This technique makes it easier to carry such food in quantity and render it readily digestible by the young.

Macaws are a South American group. The hyacinth macaw *(above right)* **is the largest parrot, at 1m long. Once widespread, the scarlet macaw** *(right)* **has declined greatly because of destruction of habitat and collection for the pet trade.**

Below right: **The black-capped lory of New Guinea lives in the canopy of forest trees where its bright plumage is an effective camouflage.**

African Grey Parrot *(Psittacus erithacus)*. Equatorial Africa.

Plum-headed Parakeet *(Psittacula cyanocephala)*. India and Sri Lanka.

Crimson-winged Parakeet *(Atros mictus)*. Australia and New Guinea.

There are nine lovebird species in Africa, some inhabiting tropical forests, others savannah woodland and lightly timbered grassland. When collecting nest material, some lovebird species tuck strips of vegetation into their body plumage rather than carrying it in their beaks. No other birds are known to do this.

Hummingbirds

Scarlet-breasted Sunbird

Green-throated Mango Hummingbird

Streamer-tailed Hummingbird

Above: **Hummingbirds are an American family; in Africa, sunbirds also feed at flowers but lack the amazing flying abilities of hummers.**

For a wide variety of American flowering plants, hummingbirds fulfil the role of insects, carrying pollen from one to another so that seed will set. In exchange, the flowers secrete nectar on which the hummers themselves depend. Hummingbird flowers are usually brightly coloured – often red and without perfume as they make no use of insects. They have long or curved trumpets, matching the beak shapes of different species of hummingbird. This means that hummers tend to feed at the sort of flower which best 'fits' their beaks, and this is necessary because otherwise pollen would be wasted and flowers would fail to produce seed and soon die out, with disastrous consequences for the hummers.

For hummingbirds to feed at flowers they have had to evolve a way of flying unique amongst birds. Each wingtip follows a flattened figure-of-eight path through the air, providing lift and propulsion on not only the downstroke, as for ordinary birds, but also on the upstroke. This gives them incredible manoeuvrability – they can stop dead in mid-air, hover and even fly backwards. Normally the wings beat at 20–80 times a second, depending on the species, and they may reach 200 beats a second when a bird is going flat out.

Not surprisingly, hummingbirds use energy very quickly and, though nectar

Above centre: **Hummingbirds beat their wings in a figure-of-eight, so that forward and backward strokes** **give lift and propulsion. By changing the angle of the wings, they can fly forwards or backwards, and hover.**

Hummingbirds' beaks have evolved to fit the trumpets of different types of flowers. The birds have extremely long tongues with which they can lap the nectar. Many species also catch insects in flight.

is very rich, they must feed every ten minutes or so throughout the day. For their size, hummers have relatively the largest hearts of any warm-blooded creatures, and they pump at 500 or more beats per second, transferring fuel from digestive system to muscles.

They are mostly tiny birds. The smallest, the Cuban bee hummingbird, has a body only 15mm long, though tail and beak make its overall length 55mm. The smaller any creature is, the more problem it has in maintaining its body temperatures in cold conditions, and hummers are no exception. If they attempted to maintain normal body temperature of 40°C (104°F) at night they would burn off their fuel reserves and die. Therefore they have to become torpid, slowing the heart beat almost to a stop and allowing their temperatures to fall – an ability shared by very few other bird species.

There are 320 species of hummingbird mostly in the northern half of South America, but some occur as far south as Tierra del Fuego. Nor has their tiny size prevented some hummers from becoming migrants. In the spring, the ruby-throated hummingbird increases its weight by more than 50% with extra fat which it uses as fuel for a 500-mile crossing of the Gulf of Mexico, undertaken non-stop in about 25 hours en route to breed in the western USA. The rufous hummer migrates along the Rockies as far as Alaska, returning to the warmth of South America each winter.

Above right: **The ruby-throated hummingbird is a summer visitor to North America. Here a female feeds her chick. Male hummers take no part in the incubation or care of young.**

Birds of paradise and bower birds

Male birds of paradise are some of the most spectacularly plumaged birds in the world and they have evolved remarkably elaborate displays in order to show themselves to best advantage.

Most of the 40 species live in New Guinea and its adjacent islands, though a few have reached northern Australia. They live in tropical forests, which experience little change in temperature from season to season and little difference in the amount of food available to living creatures. This means that in many tropical forest birds, the females are capable of rearing the young without help from the males who can afford to devote their energies to competing with each other for mates. Since the most attractive and vigorous males will be the ones which get the most females, they will pass on their talents to their offspring and gradually plumage and display will become more and more elaborate. Birds of paradise provide an extreme example of this evolutionary trend.

Living in dense forest, some species display in the tree-tops where there is ample sunlight to show off their plumage. Others display on the forest floor, choosing sunlit glades where they will clear away leaf litter and perhaps even peck off any overhanging foliage to ensure that nothing obstructs the spotlight of sunbeam in which they will sing, dance and posture. Favoured sites are used year round by the males, some of which display alone, while other species gather in groups.

Below: **Most male bower birds build and decorate elaborate structures to attract mates, as in the case of the crestless gardener which builds a 'tent' with a carefully tended garden. The females alone of both birds of paradise and bower birds are responsible for the care of eggs and young.**

Wilson's Bird of Paradise
(Diphyllodes respublica)

Little King Bird of Paradise
(Cicinnurus regius)

Superb Bird of Paradise
(Lophorina superba)

Below: a male golden bowerbird at his bower; this species is endemic to New Guinea.

Prince Rudolph's Blue
Bird of Paradise
(Paradisaea rudolphi)

Magnificent Bird of
Paradise *(Diphyllodes
magnificus)*

styles of bower. Some consist of heaped up cones of twigs joined by a display perch, while others make parallel walls of tall twigs to form an avenue. Bowers are ornamented with collected objects, some species favouring lichens or flowers, others selecting items of one colour only or painting the walls with a pulp of berry juice. One species, the Australian satin bower bird, is reputed occasionally to use a piece of bark as a brush to spread its paint.

Like birds of paradise, male bower birds take no part in domestic affairs once mating has been accomplished.

Male birds of paradise have developed elaborate plumages and individual displays. Perhaps the most bizarre is the blue bird of paradise *(right)*, which hangs upside down, singing and swinging itself to and fro.

Hybridisation between different species of birds is generally almost unknown, but it evidently occurs frequently in birds of paradise. As the females of many species are dully plumaged and similar in appearance, confusion on the part of the males might be understandable and rather suggests that the females themselves are, at least, absent-minded in their mating habits. It is normally assumed that there is a good reason for every adaptation in nature, but it is difficult to see what advantage hybridisation can confer on the individual species involved, especially because the individual species would become extinct if it happened too frequently.

Male bower birds are, if anything, more remarkable than birds of paradise. Instead of evolving remarkable plumage, they actually build elaborate structures on which to base courtship. There are 19 species in New Guinea and Australia, and different species construct different

Magnificent Bird of Paradise displaying

Temperate grasslands

Below right: **Small grassland species, such as the skylark, are usually well camouflaged and declare their ownership of territory by songflights.**

Below: **Preferring to run rather than fly, male great bustards display on the ground, fanning out white feathers which are normally concealed beneath camouflaged plumage. Formerly widespread across the grasslands of Europe and southern Asia, bustards have been largely exterminated by man in many areas.**

Where rainfall is too limited to support forests, the habitats are dominated by grasses or by dwarf shrubs such as heather or sage brush. Trees do grow, but they tend to be stunted or scattered except along river valleys where they can draw on the higher water table in the ground. Generally, summers are hot and the winters are cold. Rainfall occurs mainly in spring and is followed by a flush of new plant growth and a consequent increase in food, mostly in the form of small seeds or ground-living insects and other invertebrates. The rains

can be very heavy while they last, flooding low-lying ground to create temporary wetland habitats. At this season, many birds migrate into the temperate grasslands, including waterfowl which will breed in the marshes before they dry out.

The lack of trees over huge areas has major effects on the birds' breeding habits. Nests on the ground are particularly vulnerable, not only to predators but to the feet of grazing herbivores, and in many species the young leave their nests as soon as they are hatched in order to reduce the risk of total loss. Birds of prey,

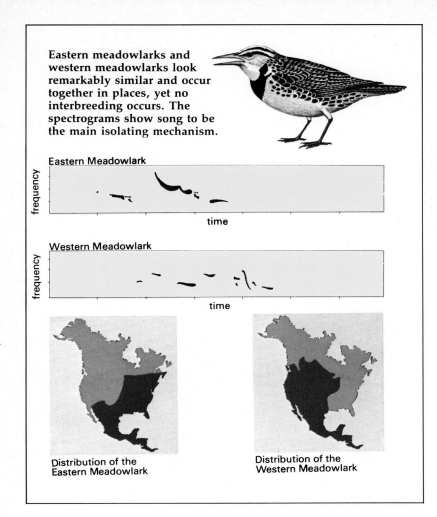

Eastern meadowlarks and western meadowlarks look remarkably similar and occur together in places, yet no interbreeding occurs. The spectrograms show song to be the main isolating mechanism.

Eastern Meadowlark

frequency

time

Western Meadowlark

frequency

time

Distribution of the Eastern Meadowlark

Distribution of the Western Meadowlark

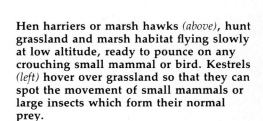

Hen harrier

Hen harriers or marsh hawks *(above)*, hunt grassland and marsh habitat flying slowly at low altitude, ready to pounce on any crouching small mammal or bird. Kestrels *(left)* hover over grassland so that they can spot the movement of small mammals or large insects which form their normal prey.

which mostly favour tree or cliff sites for breeding, are less common in areas far from such sites but some, such as the steppe eagle, will build on the ground.

Birds of prey, being large and conspicuous, can advertise their ownership of a territory by display flights but small birds must sing to make their presence known. And since singing from the ground does not carry far, larks and others ascend into the sky and sing from on high.

Species whose young are not adapted to leave the next immediately after hatching seek nesting sites which are well concealed and sheltered from sun or rain. Burrows are attractive for this reason. The American burrowing owl digs its own or lives in holes made by mammals such as prairie dogs. Bee eaters, which feed on large insects caught in flight, excavate tunnels in steep banks and are often found along rivers, where suitable soft earth banks occur most frequently.

Just as birds are capable of coping with extremes of temperature or food shortage, so in grassland habitats they show themselves well able to devise means of getting round the problems caused by lack of cover and suitable nest sites.

Common Kestrel

Below: **The meadow pipit** *(right)* **favours dry grassland in Europe but the yellow wagtail** *(left)* **prefers damp grassland, especially where grazing livestock attract copious insects.**

Below right: **Flock pigeons, like many other Australian grass species, are nomadic and move around in large groups following the infrequent rains to feed on young leaves and seeds.**

Yellow Wagtail

Meadow Pipit

Flock pigeon

Birds of prey

Most creatures which are hunted are constantly alert for danger. Many are skilled at concealment or rarely venture into the open. Some are well-equipped to defend themselves. Despite this, birds of prey seem able to find and kill their food almost without effort and some species have become such skilful hunters that they can overpower creatures far larger than themselves.

Worldwide, there are about 250 species of bird of prey, hunting practically every living land creature from dragonflies to deer: even fish are not safe.

The habitats in which birds of prey hunt and their favoured prey both influence their shape and habits. Generally, eagles live in open country, covering large territories with little effort by soaring and gliding on long, broad wings. They capture medium-sized mammals, reptiles and birds on the ground, sometimes after a plunge from high altitude but often after a deliberately devious approach at low level to take the intended prey by surprise. Buzzards are smaller and take correspondingly smaller prey.

Harriers and kites also take prey on the ground but their technique is to fly slowly over grassland and marshes at low altitude, gliding and circling on long wings as they peer into the vegetation for frogs, voles and small birds. Hawks and falcons specialise in catching birds and insects in flight. Living in open habitats, falcons have long wings designed for rapid acceleration over short distances – in a power dive, a peregrine falcon can reach speeds reputedly as high as 300kph! By contrast, hawks' wings are rounded, which slows them but aids manoeuvrability as they hunt prey through woodland cover.

The legs and beaks of birds of prey reflect their killing techniques. An eagle tackling large prey will hurtle into it at high speed, adding to its impact by kicking forward with both feet to knock its victim off balance: its feet and legs are correspondingly powerful. By contrast, hawks and harriers all have slender legs and long, thin toes – suited to reaching out for small, evasive creatures. The kill is normally made by driving in the talons

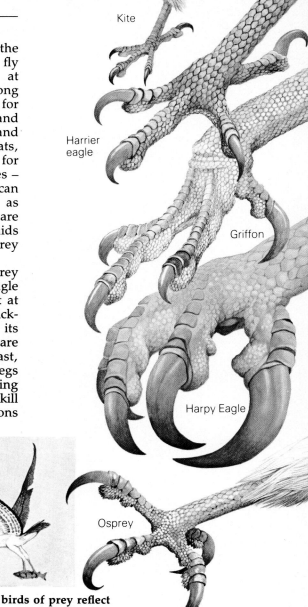

Kite

Harrier eagle

Griffon

Harpy Eagle

Osprey

Above: **The feet of birds of prey reflect their hunting styles and the size of prey they take. The griffon vulture's feet are relatively weak and short-taloned, because it does not kill prey. Unlike owls, birds of prey strike their quarry with three toes forward and one back.**

Left: **A male bat falcon, a South American forest species, passes prey to its mate.**

Below: **a martial eagle striking at a guinea fowl.**

Top: **Though able to kill prey, many eagles – like these American bald eagles – also regularly feed on carrion.**

and, though falcons will sometimes finish off their victims by biting through the neck vertebrae, birds of prey normally use their beaks only for feeding. Hooking in the sharp upper mandible and holding down the carcass under foot, they tear off lumps of flesh.

Birds of prey have remarkable eyesight. Their vision is at least four times, and perhaps as much as eight times, as acute as man's. In practical terms, that would enable an eagle to see a hare more than 1·5km away. Equipped as they are, it is small wonder that birds of prey are such efficient hunters.

Above: **Many birds of prey seem to do aerobatics for pleasure and some have spectacular display flights. Here a courting pair of bald eagles tumbles through the air with claws interlocked.**

Right: **Goshawks hunt prey of pigeon and squirrel size in woodland.**

Savannah

Savannah grasslands occur on a large scale in tropical and sub-tropical zones where, though the temperature remains fairly high all year, rain ralls only in summer. Forming a transition between forest at one extreme and desert at the other, savannahs may carry large numbers of well-spaced trees or, in the dryer areas, only small and scattered thorn bushes.

The food resources are less restricted than in temperate grasslands, partly because of the greater tree cover and partly because reptiles are common. Many birds of prey catch snakes and seem to have no trouble dealing with venomous species. This is less surprising than it seems: clearly birds of prey must be able to despatch all sorts of quarry without being bitten or injured, or they would risk incapacitation and possibly death every time they make a kill.

Raptors are generally common in savannah habitats. In Africa, the long-legged secretary bird hunts insects, small mammals and reptiles on the ground, killing larger prey with strong blows from its feet. In the air, falcons hunt

The long-legged secretary bird is a specialist predator of the African savannah – here it is killing a python.

1 The Parson Finch *(Poephilia cincta)*, Australia.
2-8 Varieties of waxbill:
2 Red-eared, or Common, Waxbill *(Estrilda troglodytes)*, Central Africa.
3 Golden-breasted *(Estrilda subflavia)*, West Africa.
4 Yellow-bellied *(Estrilda melanotis quartinia)*, West Africa.
5 Orange-cheeked *(Estrilda melpoda)*, West Africa.

Tropical grassland produce vast crops of seeds which are the food for many species of small birds such as these African waxbill species and the Australian parson finch.

Left: **The vulturine guinea fowl feeds on seeds and invertebrates in the African savannah. In turn, it is an important prey of the martial eagle and of small cats such as the serval.**

50

The lilac-breasted roller *(left)* and red-billed hornbill *(right)* are two African birds which feed on small reptiles and mammals, insects and berries.

6 Crimson-rumped *(Estrilda rhodopyga)*, East Africa.
7 St Helena *(Estrilda astrild)*, Central Africa.
8 Black-cheeked | *(Estrilda erythronotos)*, South-western Africa.

other birds and large flying insects. When termites are mating and huge swarms leave the nest mounds, many birds gather to feed on them, including even eagles which find the huge numbers of termites ample compensation for their small size.

Where there are large grazing herbivores, there are large numbers of insects which lay eggs in their droppings or on the animals themselves. Flycatchers, such as the South American cattle tyrant, will move with the grazing animals, often riding on their backs, to catch insects that are associated with them or are disturbed from the grass by their feet. Cattle egrets feed on insects, lizards and frogs flushed by grazing animals and will also pick

Left: **The Australian kookaburra is a species of kingfisher which feeds by pouncing on small mammals and reptiles.**

parasites from the animals themselves so that the relationship is of mutual benefit. The spread of stock farming has provided them with a new opportunity and in the last 40 years they have spread from their original range in Africa and Asia to North and South America, Indonesia, Australia and New Zealand.

The savannahs are a major wintering ground for migrants from temperate woodlands and grasslands. They arrive in the habitat during the rainy season when sufficient surplus food is available to support them in addition to the breeding populations of resident birds. Once the food resources start to decline these birds will be on the way north again, back on their own breeding grounds.

Below: **The African oxpeckers, distantly related to starlings, feed exclusively on the external parasites of large herbivores, including domestic species, and are built rather like woodpeckers with sharp claws to hang on and a stiffened tail to give support.**

Ratites

The disadvantage of flight is that it limits the ability of birds to grow very large. Those which have done so have lost, or perhaps never possessed, the power to fly. Five bird families, known as the ratites, have flat breast-bones unsuitable for supporting wing muscles: ostrich, rheas, cassowaries, emu and kiwis.

Largest of all the world's birds is the ostrich. Males may stand up to 2·75m tall and weigh up to 154 kg. Living in the open savannah and semi-desert regions of Africa, their great height enables them to spot approaching predators at long range and to make off at speeds of up to 70kph. Their muscular legs are bare so

that they do not overheat when running fast, and their feet have only two toes, more like the hoof of an antelope than the foot of a normal bird.

An adult male ostrich will mate with three or more hens. One of these has a superior status in the group and it is she, not the male, who decides which subor-

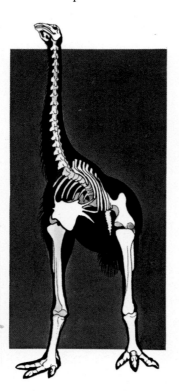

The Giant Moa stood nearly 4 metres tall.

Australian Cassowary

Male ostrich with females

dinate hens may join. All the hens lay their eggs in one nest after which the subordinate females are driven off. Then male and female share incubation of the clutch, which may amount to as many as 25 eggs. The hen, being relatively camouflaged, sits by day and the male sits by night. The young birds can run and fend for themselves from birth: at a month old they can reach speeds of 50kph though they are not fully grown until 18 months. It is normal for family parties to join up and for some adults to leave their young when this happens, so that dozens of immature birds of all ages and sizes may be in the care of just a couple of adults.

The grasslands of Australia support the emu and those of South America have two species of rhea. Australia also holds a giant forest bird – the cassowary; a second species occurs in New Guinea and a third in New Britain. All three species have horny 'helmets' supposedly

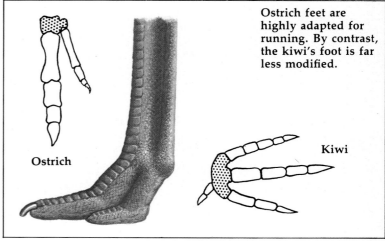

Ostrich feet are highly adapted for running. By contrast, the kiwi's foot is far less modified.

Ostrich

Kiwi

as a protection against injury when running through undergrowth and low branches. These aggressive and powerful birds can inflict severe injuries by kicking and have killed a number of humans.

Formerly, New Zealand held a remarkable family of huge flightless birds, the moas, but these were exterminated by the Maoris after their arrival there about a thousand years ago. Today, New Zealand's only surviving ratites are the chicken-sized kiwis, which are nocturnal inhabitants of the evergreen forests.

Three ratites of Australasia – the forest-dwelling cassowary; the emu of the open grassland and the nocturnal kiwi, the national emblem of New Zealand. The New Zealand forests were once the homes of giant moas – huge flightless birds

Emu with chicks

Kiwi

Deserts

Deserts cover a fifth of the world's land surface, occurring in Africa, Asia, both the Americas and Australia. Rainfall is rare, but when it comes may be torrential. Daytime temperatures are high and the ground surface can become fiercely hot, but at night temperatures plummet. Vegetation is sparse or absent except along the beds of seasonal rivers or around oases.

Despite its apparent inhospitality, a variety of birds live in the desert. Here, as in other habitats, the insulating qualities of feathers helps them to cope with extremes of temperature. At night, they can fluff up their plumage so that it holds still air and enables them to keep warm; in the daytime they can slick it down so that the insulating pockets of air are squeezed out and their bodies can radiate excess heat. Desert species tend to be smaller than their counterparts in warmer habitats, following the rule that smaller creatures radiate warmth more than larger ones. If they are in danger of overheating, they pant so that air flowing over the moist throat surfaces causes evaporation and consequent cooling.

Dehydration is perhaps a bigger problem than heat itself. Water is hard to obtain and cooling by panting uses up body fluids. However, some desert species are so well adapted that they can lose up to

Cock pintailed sandgrouse and a well-camouflaged chick. Widespread across North Africa and the Middle East, this species also occurs in arid parts of Spain and southern France.

half their weight through dehydration and still recover once they drink. The problem is greatest for seed-eaters because their food is so dry. Sandgrouse will make daily round trips of up to 100km to drink. By bathing and saturating their belly feathers, the males can carry back adequate supplies of water for their young, which sip it out of their parents' plumage. Other seed-eaters feed their young on insects, which contain adequate moisture.

Many desert birds are powerful runners. For example, the roadrunner, a North American cuckoo that preys on reptiles and invertebrates, is a bantam-sized bird that can run at up to 30kph. It has a long tail which acts as a rudder to give it considerable manoeuvrability so that it can evade most ground predators without deigning to fly. Nonetheless, for most desert birds, good flying abilities are essential in order to reach the thinly scattered resources of food and water.

Breeding is related to rainfall rather than seasons. When rains do come, many species pair and begin nestbuilding within hours; no time can be lost if the young are to hatch while plants and insect life are still briefly abundant.

Above: **A North American species, the mourning dove can tolerate severe dehydration. Seed-eaters themselves, like other pigeons they feed their chicks by regurgitating a liquid 'milk' which ensures that they do not lack moisture.**

Below: **Desert larks of North Africa and the Middle East have well camouflaged plumage. Those that live in areas where the sand and rocks are dark coloured have darker plumages than those which live where the ground is paler.**

Vultures

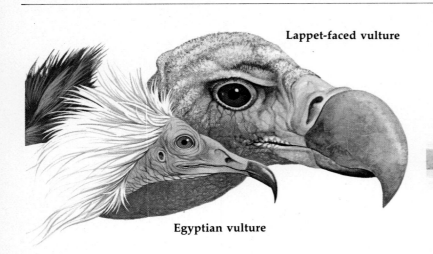

Lappet-faced vulture

Egyptian vulture

Turkey vulture

Greater yellow-headed vulture

Below: **Vultures squabble over a zebra: generally, small species make way for larger ones and late arrivals chase off those which have already fed. Thus all individuals get their turn, quickly stripping the carcass of its bones: 1 Ruppell's vulture; 2 immature Ruppell's vulture; 3 lappet-faced vulture; 4 immature lappet-faced vulture; 5 white-headed vulture; 6 Egyptian vulture; 7 white-backed vulture; 8 hooded vultures.**

Above: **Lappet-faced vultures feed mainly on muscle torn from large carcasses. Egyptian vultures pick fragments from the bones and can scavenge successfully at rubbish heaps.**

Every creature dies eventually, usually by falling prey to some other animal, but sometimes simply of disease or age. A number of different kinds of birds (including ravens, crows, golden eagles and gulls) are not slow to feed on carcasses or the remains of kills made by other creatures. One group of birds (the vultures), specialises in feeding exclusively on carrion.

Because vultures do not kill their own food, depending instead on the misfortunes of others to provide them with their meals, they cannot rely on being able to eat every day. Consequently, they are all fairly large to be able to live off their own fat reserves for days at a time. They have also evolved a very economical way of flying, which they share with other large birds of prey. Having large, broad wings they are able to float on the rising air currents, or thermals, which occur when the sun warms the land surface and causes the air above it to heat and rise up. Upcurrents which can be used by vultures also occur in mountainous areas where wind strikes the rising ground and is forced upwards. As a result, vultures are largely confined to the hot plains of Africa, southern Asia and the southern USA, though a few species live in southern Europe and along the mountain backbone of the Americas. The Andean condor is one of the largest of all flying birds, with a wingspan of 3m.

Most common where large grazing animals are abundant and provide a good source of carrion, vultures rely largely on their keen eyesight to find food. Soaring

Black vulture

The Californian condor is one of the world's rarest birds. Vultures are declining world-wide as man reduces their available food supply.

The New World vultures are not related to those of the Old World, but have evolved similar adaptations because they feed in a similar way.

at high altitude, they doubtless often see predators make their kills and swiftly descend to wait, at a safe distance, until they can take their turn. Soaring vultures also keep a close eye on their neighbours and, if one sees another descend to the ground, it will swiftly glide over to investigate. Very quickly, birds from a wide area will arrive on the scene.

Different species have different shaped beaks, adapted to feeding on different parts of a carcass. Some can consume tough hide, others only strip off flesh from the bones. One, the lammergeier, has a scoop-shaped tongue that enables it to extract the marrow from bones. Because its feeding habits are different from most vultures, it lacks the bare head and neck which is the trademark of vultures, a hygienic adaptation to prevent plumage from being fouled by blood as these remarkable birds carry out their necessary function of disposing of carcasses.

Opposite: **Few birds use tools, but some Egyptian vultures learn to break ostrich eggs by dropping stones on them.**

Right: **Old World vultures generally clear carrion while it is still fresh but New World species, like this male king vulture, tend to have weaker beaks and can only tackle rotten meat. Unusually for birds, they have a well-developed sense of smell which probably helps them to find their food.**

Temperate wetlands

Wetlands are often very productive habitats with abundant plants, small invertebrates and fish – a rich opportunity for any land creature which can adapt to life in the water. The main problem to overcome is how to avoid getting cold, particularly in temperate and tundra wetlands where water temperatures are low. Generally, mammals were slow to colonise wetlands because their fur gave them little protection against wetting and becoming chilled. By contrast, birds were ready equipped with a fairly waterproof outer coat of feathers. Even now, the plumage of waterfowl is not very different from that of land birds; the former merely have a denser coat of down to give better insulation against the cold, and a rather smoother and tighter-fitting coat of contour feathers.

By the time a few mammals had evolved a system of trapping air in their pelts, so as to waterproof themselves,

birds had already moved into most of the different wetland feeding niches and mammals have been unable to oust them.

Though there are many wetland bird species, most of them, whatever their evolutionary origins, conform to one of two shapes – 'duck' or 'wader'.

The 'duck' shape of divers, grebes, wildfowl (and many seabirds too) is suited to swimming on or under the water. The body is streamlined. The feet of many species are webbed: when the bird brings its foot forward, the toes come together so that the webs fold and the foot turns back to be pulled through the water with minimal resistance; on the backstroke, the whole foot unfolds and becomes a rigid paddle pushing against the water. The toes of coot are not joined by webs but have lobed sides. These are less efficient for swimming but are better than webs on land, where coots sometimes feed.

Left: **The osprey is one of the few birds of prey which catches fish, sometimes plunging its whole body beneath the surface to grasp them in its talons.**

Shoveler has large bill which it uses to sift the surface of the water for floating food; its bill has a series of filters that allow the water to run out but retain food

Tufted duck is diving duck feeding on small invertebrates beneath the surface

Mute swan feeds from the surface but its very long neck enables it to reach food farther beneath the surface than other surface-feeders

Opposite: **Few small birds enter the water because their size makes it difficult for them to keep warm. One exception is the kingfisher, which plunges briefly beneath the surface to grab unwary fish. Other members of the kingfisher family catch small reptiles by dropping from their perches so it is easy to see how kingfishers extended this habit to catch fish.**

Below: **A group of European waterbirds illustrates the different ways in which the species divide up the feeding habitat, so minimising competition between them.**

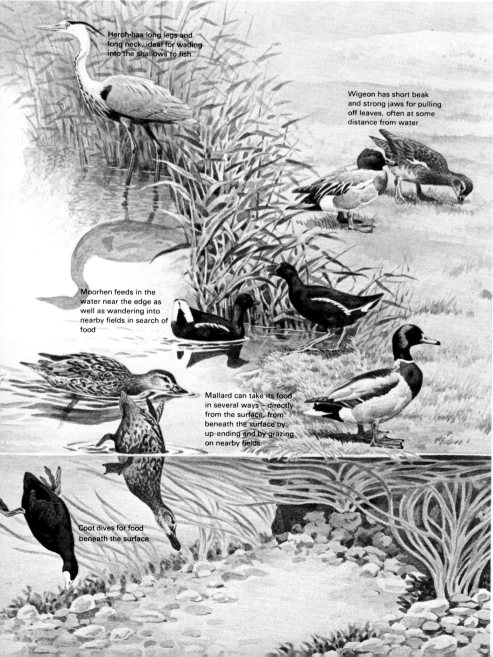

Heron has long legs and long neck, ideal for wading into the shallows to fish

Wigeon has short beak and strong jaws for pulling off leaves, often at some distance from water

Moorhen feeds in the water near the edge as well as wandering into nearby fields in search of food

Mallard can take its food in several ways – directly from the surface, from beneath the surface by up-ending and by grazing on nearby fields

Coot dives for food beneath the surface

Above: **The grey heron of Europe and Asia is one of 63 species worldwide that feed on fish, frogs, small mammals and birds at the water margin.**

The legs of most waterbirds are placed well to the rear of the body because this gives them efficient propulsion in swimming. The disadvantage is that it tends to make them ungainly and slow-moving on land. To avoid this difficulty, birds such as waders and herons (which feed in the shallows and need to be able to move easily on land as well as in water) have developed long legs so that they do not have to swim at all. Their feet are usually long-toed to support them on soft ground, while their long legs and beaks enable them to catch creatures below the surface of the water or mud.

Though temperate wetlands are colder and may freeze in winter, the opportunities they offer are much like those of wetlands in warmer countries. As a result, species of waterfowl and wading birds with broadly similar adaptations are found worldwide, from tundra pools to tropical swamps.

Tropical wetlands

The world's tropical wetlands are even richer than the temperate wetlands. Their warmth and the long growing season support luxuriant plant life and great numbers of invertebrates, both of which provide food for myriads of fish, all three in turn supporting a diversity of birds.

One feature of tropical waters is that during the heat of the day many fish rise to bask just below the surface. The skimmer takes advantage of this habit. Its beak is much longer in the lower mandible than the upper one and it flies low across the water with its bill wide open, the lower half cutting the surface in a long line. Each time it touches a fish, the bird snaps its head up to flip the fish out of the water and swallow it. The jacanas feed very differently. They have extraordinarily long toes and claws to support them as they run over lily pads where they seek invertebrates and tiny frogs.

The African jacana sometimes carries its chicks beneath its wings.

Pelicans use the huge sac which hangs from the lower mandible as a kind of net to capture their food. Some, such as the white pelican, fish cooperatively. A group of five or more birds will swim along in horseshoe formation, herding fish in front of them: then all the birds plunge in their beaks together, scooping at the gathered shoal before it can escape.

The African jacana or lily-trotter carrying its young under its wing.

Three species of skimmer occur in tropical wetlands: the black skimmer *(top)* in the Americas, the African skimmer *(centre)* and the Indian skimmer *(bottom).*

Like all pelicans, the grey *(right)* and pink-backed *(left)* pelicans use their huge beaks as nets to scoop up fish.

Despite their size – the greater flamingo stands nearly 1·5m tall – all four flamingo species feed only on tiny creatures which they collect by filtering water through sieves inside their beaks. Greater and lesser flamingoes sometimes occur together, but they do not compete for food. Greater flamingoes have fairly coarse filters in their beaks and take mainly insect larvae and other small animals which they find in the mud. This means that they can only feed where the water is shallow enough for them to

Below left: **Many large wetland species, like the scarlet ibis, nest colonially in trees to obtain security from predators.**

reach the bottom by wading or by swimming and upending. In contrast, lesser flamingoes have finer filters and feed on algae which float in profusion throughout the waters so that they can feed in any situation.

The flamingoes' feeding habits allow them to exploit a kind of wetland which few other creatures can tolerate – the great salt lakes which are so alkaline that no plants or fish can live in them, but rich in tiny shrimps. Here flamingoes find not only food but safety for breeding, building their nests of mud and stones in colonies which, in Africa, may

be up to a million birds strong. As summer goes on, the shallow waters around the colony slowly dry up, so that when the young birds leave their nests they must travel far to feed themselves. As they cannot yet fly, they must walk all the way. On the Etosha Pan in South West Africa, a group of over 20 000 lesser flamingo chicks were observed to walk 80km in a month to reach water and throughout their journey they were fed by their parents, which flew back and forth shuttling food supplies to them – a stunning example of the bond between parent birds and their young.

The flamingo feeds with its head partly or wholly underwater and the beak upside down. By waggling its tongue it swooshes water in and out between its mandibles, fine sieves inside the bill trapping minute food items so that the bird can swallow them.

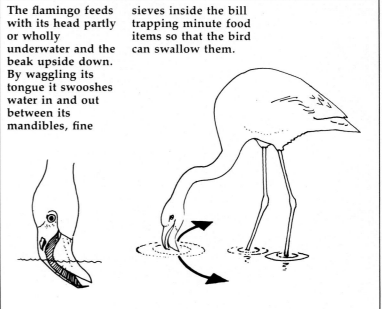

Shore birds

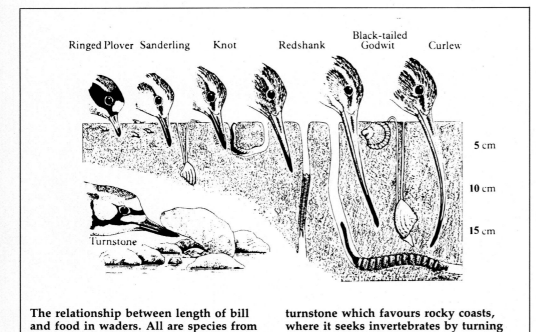

The relationship between length of bill and food in waders. All are species from sandy or muddy shores except the turnstone which favours rocky coasts, where it seeks invertebrates by turning over seaweed and stones.

Every autumn, vast numbers of wading birds move into mild coastal habitats to pass the winter. Some travel from breeding grounds on the tundra far into the southern hemisphere, but many remain in Europe and North America, especially on estuaries.

Here, the interaction of river and sea produces great expanses of mud on which live innumerable millions of shell fish and marine worms. As the tide goes out, uncovering the mudflats, busy flocks of waders follow close behind. Some, like the sanderling, hasten along seeming to probe almost at random for small snails just below the surface. Others, such as the curlew, probe deliberately and deep where the tell-tale casts on the mud betray the lugworm in its burrow beneath. A third group, including the ringed plover, characteristically stand motionless until they spot some movement by a creature at the surface of the mud and then run swiftly forward to capture it.

Oystercatchers take the larger shellfish, such as cockles or mussels. These are difficult prey to deal with and though some oystercatchers learn how to snip skilfully through the muscle with which these bivalves hold their shells shut, other birds simply hammer away with

Left: **Even closely related species avoid competition through different feeding strategies. Spotted redshank will wade deeper than redshank or greenshank, while all three have different length beaks so that they take prey from different depths in the mud.**

Opposite: **The extremely long-legged black-winged stilt feeds on brown shrimps, tadpoles, small fish and insect larvae.**

Below: **Estuaries offer wide areas of rich feeding for enormous winter flocks of waders and wildfowl.**

their beaks to break the shells. This works, but eventually their beaks are worn down and they may not be able to feed so efficiently.

At high tide, shore birds gather in huge roosts, great numbers resting together on open ground where predators cannot approach unseen. If they are driven to take flight, they will often wheel and turn low over the sea in a tight-packed flock; their reactions are so quick that all the birds seem to move as one, the whole flock changing colour in an instant as the birds change direction and show light bellies instead of dark backs.

Feeding with the tides, all these birds are regularly active at night, especially in the depths of winter. Then low temperatures mean they need more food to keep warm just when their prey is getting scarce and cold is driving it to burrow deeper in the mud.

In the breeding season, most shore birds move away from the coast, either moving inland to damp grasslands and marshes or undertaking the long migration north to the tundra.

Shorebirds are part of a group of nearly 200 species generally known as waders, though by no means all of them wade or live in wetland habitats. The group includes species as diverse as the jacana and the stone curlews, most of which live in dry, sandy wastes.

Below: **Painted snipe are skulking birds, rarely emerging from the cover of heavily vegetated swamps.**

Bottom: **Some waders, such as the golden plover, will attempt to distract predators from their young by feigning injury, flopping awkwardly over the ground until they have drawn the danger off to a safe distance.**

Sandwich Tern

Grey Plover

Sanderling

Painted snipe

male

female

Golden plover

The oceans

Two-thirds of the earth's surface is covered by the seas. The most productive areas are the polar waters and off the west coasts of South Africa and South America, because in these areas winds and currents cause nutrient-rich water to well up from the ocean bed. This supports an abundance of plankton which in turn is preyed on by fish, squid, seals, porpoises and whales, and great numbers of birds. By contrast, tropical oceans hold little marine life and birds are sparse except around islands.

Most seabirds spend much time on or under the water and must be well insulated with fat and waterproof plumage. Flight requires a light body structure and this also gives buoyancy which is a disadvantage to diving birds. They tend to have heavier bones and smaller air sacs than normal. The Galapagos cormorant has abandoned the power of flight so as to be able to reduce its buoyancy. It floats with its back awash and can dive with little effort. Other cormorants deliberately wet their plumages to aid diving and when they come ashore must stand with their wings held out to dry.

Cormorants use their feet for propulsion under water. However, most seabirds which actively pursue their prey beneath the surface swim with their wings, which must be fairly short and paddle-like. This in turn affects their flying ability so that, though they can get along quite rapidly with a direct, whirring flight low over the surface, they lack manoeuvrability and agility in the air.

Many species feed by plunging from the air after fish which they can see just beneath the surface. Gannets and boobys have strengthened skulls and foreparts to absorb the shock of impact. They keep their wings spread for course correction until the last moment, folding them back to the shape of a paper dart as they hit the surface. To protect their eyes underwater, they close the nictitating membrane: this is a special inner eyelid which all birds possess and use to clean their eyes or to protect them from damage. In diving birds, the membrane has a clear central lens so that in effect they wear goggles while underwater.

Birds cannot penetrate deep beneath the oceans and the range of niches for them to exploit is far fewer than on land. As a result, there are less than 300 seabird species in the world, compared with over 8300 land birds. However, several seabird species are far more numerous than any land birds because their habitat is so enormous: the Wilson's storm petrel, a south Atlantic species, is probably the world's most numerous wild bird.

The brown booby and masked booby both feed by plunge diving. Related to the gannets, they replace them in tropical waters.

Gannet feeds on larger fish such as pollack and mackerel, that feed near the surface, catching them in its bill

Arctic tern plunges to the surface to catch small fish and marine creatures

Storm petrel uses its feet to patter along the surface, disturbing plankton and small fish which it then catches in its bill

Guillemot dives from the surface, using its wings to swim underwater for up to a minute, and feeding mainly on small fish found in shoals

Eider duck

Black-throated diver

The eider is a sea duck which feeds by diving for shellfish. Black-throated divers breed on lakes, mainly in tundra, but winter on the sea.

In this North Atlantic scene, several species of seabird are feeding together – a not uncommon situation when fish shoals are close to the surface.

Arctic skua chases other seabirds, making them disgorge their food and catching it in mid-air

Cormorant is larger than the shag and its plumage traps very little air, reducing its buoyancy and allowing it to dive deeper and feed on flatfish and other bottom feeders

Fulmar has learned to scavenge on the small fish and offal thrown overboard from fishing boats

Shag is streamlined and underwater uses its large, webbed feet to propel it; it feeds on small fish, such as sand-eels

The cape cormorant of South Africa and the guanay cormorant of South America are both important producers of guano – the accumulated droppings of huge seabird colonies which are a valuable fertiliser.

Tubenoses

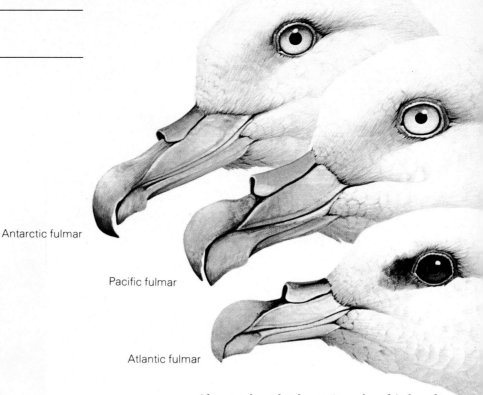

Antarctic fulmar

Pacific fulmar

Atlantic fulmar

Giant petrel

Cape pigeon

Silver- grey fulmar

Above: **Three antarctic tubenoses. The giant petrel often preys on other birds and scavenges carcasses; the cape pigeon feeds mainly on plankton and fish but will also scavenge; the fulmar feeds mainly on surface plankton.**

About a hundred species of seabird, collectively known as tubenoses, have beaks which are made of distinct plates with the nostrils encased in large tubes. The purpose of this feature is unclear. It may assist in scenting food, as some species feed on the sea's surface at night, or it may be a device for sensing tiny changes in air pressure and so help those birds which habitually fly right amongst the waves.

Either way, it proves the relationship between birds as different in size and way of life as the albatrosses and diving petrels – birds which have evolved very different adaptations in order to exploit different opportunities at sea.

By becoming large, the albatrosses have gained certain advantages. They can take bigger food than most other seabirds so they avoid some competition. They are fairly safe from predators and, being long-lived, they need to produce only a few young to maintain their numbers. However, they have been able to grow so large only be evolving a method of flight which uses very little energy but

Petrels habitually feed by fluttering just above the waves to pick plankton from the surface. Wilson's petrel is probably the most numerous bird in the world.

Wilson's petrel

Opposite left: **There are three species of fulmar, in the Antarctic, Pacific and Atlantic. Each has a slightly different beak, perhaps reflecting differences in food or feeding methods.**

Right: **Grey-headed albatrosses and black-browed albatrosses at their nesting colony. Because of their great wingspan and dependence on strong winds, albatrosses must nest in open, windswept situations.**

which has made them dependent on strong winds (see diagram). This means that albatrosses are largely confined to the southern oceans where winds blow almost constantly. Most species have been unable to cross the calm tropical seas and colonise the northern oceans.

The smaller shearwaters, so named for the habit in some species of flying low between the wave tops, depend less on constant wind and so are a far more widespread group. The disadvantage of smaller size is that they are very vulnerable to predators when on land. As a result, most of the smaller tubenoses nest in burrows or rock crevices on islands where there are no predatory mammals and, by coming and going only at night, also avoid attacks from gulls and skuas.

At the other extreme from albatrosses, the diving petrels of the Antarctic seas are small birds with short stubby wings which they use for swimming. They must whirr their wings rapidly to fly at all and, during the moult, they become entirely flightless when replacing their wing feathers.

Right: **Dynamic soaring. As soon as it has taken off, an albatross will turn into the wind with wings held out stiffly. Its weight and momentum tend to make it fall forwards through the air, and simultaneously the action of the wind against its wings tends to blow it backwards: the result is that the bird soars upwards. Then it turns partly away from the wind and flies diagonally downwards across the air current, losing height but gaining speed to give it the momentum to repeat the process. Tacking across the wind, albatrosses can fly for hours without a single flap of their wings.**

Left: **The wandering albatross has a 3·5m wingspan. Young wanderers do not breed until about seven, when they will return to the colony in which they were born.**

Seabird colonies

A seabird colony on a cliff in the eastern North Atlantic. Different species have different preferences for nest sites and together they make use of all the available space.

some breed only on islands free from predatory mammals while others choose cliff edges which are practically inaccessible except to other birds. However, many seabirds including the larger gulls and skuas are themselves active predators so that some smaller species, including puffins, nest underground in burrows or crevices. A few, such as shearwaters, also come and go only at night when their enemies are unable to hunt. By contrast, terns rely on the massed 'air power' of their colony to attack and drive off predators. So also do gulls, although each pair must also guard

Below: **Nesting guillemots and kittiwakes.**

The better adapted that birds are to life on the oceans, the less suited they are to life on land. Some are far from agile in flight and most are ungainly or slow on the ground, so they are potentially very vulnerable to predators when forced to come ashore to breed. Their choice of nesting places and their behaviour on land are dominated by this danger.

A few tropical and temperate species nest in large trees but most species live in regions where cold and high winds prevent the growth of tall vegetation near the coast. Forced to nest on the ground,

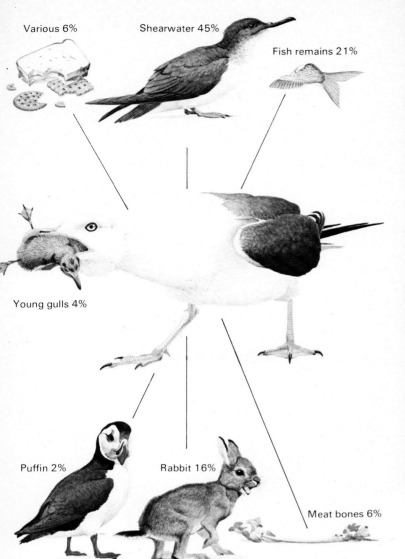

Various 6%

Shearwater 45%

Fish remains 21%

Young gulls 4%

Puffin 2%

Rabbit 16%

Meat bones 6%

Above: **A puffin with food for its young.**

Above left: **Food of the great black-backed gull at a British seabird colony.**

Below: **A sooty tern colony. Terns will mob and drive off some predators.**

its eggs and chicks from its neighbours.

Skuas and frigate birds regularly practise piracy, harrying birds bringing food to their young until they drop it. Even large birds are not safe – skuas will catch flying gannets by the wingtip so that they 'stumble' in flight and reluctantly disgorge their catch of fish. This hazard does not affect the tubenoses because they convert their food into a rich oil with which to feed the young.

Since they do not feed in individual territories around their nests, seabirds can breed close together and this partly compensates for the shortage of safe nesting areas. Even so, some species will tolerate closer spacing than others. Gannets and kittiwakes spread themselves out so that each pair is just out of pecking distance of its neighbour: by contrast, guillemots happily stand packed close together on their breeding ledges. Because each species has individual preferences for spacing and site, seabird colonies often contain a wide variety of species, each occupying a different situation. In large colonies many thousands of seabirds of many kinds may use every available nook, cranny, ledge and flat surface. For a few weeks the air is filled with birds, but once the breeding season is over most of them will disperse to sea and the colony will be deserted for another year.

Penguins

Penguins have abandoned flight altogether. By becoming heavy for their size and adapting their wings into powerful paddles, they have developed the ability to swim far faster and dive much deeper than any other birds. There are 13 species, some living in the relatively warm seas off Australia and New Zealand, South Africa and South America but others flourishing in the icy waters of Antarctica.

The largest of all is the emperor penguin, standing 1m tall and weighing about 40 kgs. For insulation and for protection against injury on the edge of the ice as they come ashore, their bodies are covered by a thick layer of fat and they are clad in dense, oily plumage. They can swim at over 40 kph, dive to at least 250m below the sea's surface and remain underwater for over 15 minutes at a time.

Ringed penguin *(top)* **and gentoo penguin in pursuit of fish. Penguins swim with their wings, which have become hard, bony flippers.**

Emperors are so big and their chicks take so long to grow to full size that they must start breeding in autumn for their young to be ready to leave them by the following summer, the season when the weather is most mild and food plentiful. When their mating season arrives, the adults leave the sea and travel across the ice, either by waddling upright or sometimes by lying on their stomachs and tobogganning quickly along, using flippers and feet to keep up their speed. The birds gather together in huge colonies of many thousand strong. By now it is June, the Antarctic winter. The female lays one

Opposite: **The emperor penguin and the smaller adelie penguin are the only two penguins which actually nest on the Antarctic continent itself. Because of the difference in their sizes, it takes emperors over a year to complete their breeding cycle whereas adelies take about six months.**

Right: **King penguins 'porpoising'; an economical mode of travel used over long distances (distance under water is 6 to 12 metres).**

egg, which the male at once takes into his care, balancing it on top of his webbed feet and squatting down so that it is warmly wrapped in the soft fold of feathers. By this time, the birds have been away from the sea for about two months, living only on fat stored in their bodies. The females have used most of their energy reserves in producing the eggs so they must now undertake the long walk back to unfrozen waters where they will feed and recover their strength.

The males incubate their eggs through winter blizzards when temperatures drop to $-60°C (-76°F)$, drowsy birds huddling together in huge groups to keep warm. As their fat reserves are used up, they slowly lose weight. At last the eggs hatch and at about the same time the females return, to regurgitate food for the newborn chicks. Now it is the males' turn to go to sea and feed for the first time in four months.

As spring advances, the sea-ice slowly melts and the adults have less far to travel between the chicks and the fishing grounds, feeding frequency increases and by mid-summer the young birds are full-grown, to be taken to sea and left to fend for themselves at the ideal time of year.

Because their breeding season is so long, a pair of Emperor penguins can, at best, produce only one chick every other year. However, because they are large and powerful birds, able to ride out foul weather at sea and outswim most predators, the adults are long-lived birds. They do not need to produce many young to keep their numbers stable.

Above: **All penguins nest in colonies. These are magellanic penguins, a South American species.**

Left: **An adelie penguin rookery. Male adelie penguins return to the breeding grounds before the females and establish their rights to a small patch of ground. Thus courtship can proceed without too much time wasted on territorial conflict between different pairs.**

Aerial birds

More than any other birds, swifts are designed for high-speed flight in pursuit of insects. Their wings are long and slender, their eyesight keen and their mouths enormous to scoop up small creatures in the air without pausing. When collecting food for their chicks, they store up the insects in a pouch in the floor of the mouth, enabling them to reduce the number of trips between feeding areas and nest sites. This is particularly important after summer rainstorms, which may temporarily clear the air of insects and force the birds to hunt far afield.

The Eurasian swift is believed to live almost its entire life on the wing. At night, instead of going to roost the birds ascend to high altitude at dusk, descending again soon after first light. Swifts' legs are so short and their wings so long that if one does accidentally land on the ground it cannot easily take off again. They mate in flight and select nest sites placed over a vertical drop, allowing the birds to fly in non-stop and, when leaving, to simply drop into the air beneath. This means of course that young birds must be able to fly well from the moment they abandon the nest.

Several kinds of swift, including the North American chimney swifts, use their own saliva as a glue to fix their nests in the best location for a clear high speed approach. The palm swift of Africa and Asia sticks its nest to the underside of a hanging palm leaf and then uses saliva to glue its eggs into the nest itself. The incubating bird has to cling on and so do

Above: **The cave swiftlet of south-east Asia constructs its nest entirely of its own saliva. The nests form the basis of birds' nest soup.**

Left: **Common swift** *(top),* **house martin** *(centre),* **European nightjar** *(bottom).* **Aerial feeders have very large gapes with which to scoop up insects in flight. In some species, such as the nightjars, the gape is surrounded by bristles to prevent prey escaping.**

Right: **Swallows feed on insects but are much less aerial than swifts, regularly perching and even landing on the ground to collect mud for nesting material.**

Swifts which breed in Europe must migrate south in autumn when aerial insects become scarce. The pallid swift *(far right)* winters in the Sudan and its breeding range extends to just north of the Mediterranean. The Alpine swift *(centre)* winters in tropical Africa and breeds in mountains no further north than Switzerland. The European swift *(below)* winters in southern Africa and its breeding range extends as far north as Lapland.

Right: The Asian crested swift constructs a tiny nest just large enough for a single egg, cemented in place with saliva.

the chicks, especially when it is windy and the nest may be blown upside down.

Cave swiftlets often nest in great numbers in total darkness. Instead of relying on eyesight they use echo location to avoid colliding with the cave walls or with each other. Each bird makes clicking sounds at a rate of about 250 clicks a second, and at the same time listens for the returning echoes, so as to judge its distance from solid objects.

Apart from swifts, many other groups of birds take insects on the wing, including swallows and martins, nightjars and flycatchers: however, none is so perfectly adapted to an aerial existence. As a group, swifts are the fastest of all birds. The needle-tailed swifts of Africa and Asia are believed to achieve speeds of up to 170 kph in level flight.

Urban birds

Man's management of the environment has generally been to the disadvantage of birds. Woodlands have been replaced by farms, and sometimes by desert. Natural forests have been changed into managed plantations; marshes have been drained; the seas overfished; and country turned into town. Almost always, complex natural systems have been replaced by simple ones from which man reaps the maximum harvest. There are fewer niches available for birds. However, the new conditions have ideally suited the needs of some species which have become numerous and widespread as a result.

House sparrows have a long association with man. They evolved as seed-eaters in arid habitats, probably in the Middle East. As early man began to grow crops, so the sparrow learned to steal his grain and when farms spread across Eu-

Above: **Robins feed on the ground, seeking small invertebrates. These are scarce in winter so all robins, male and female, defend individual feeding territories at this season, driving off intruders.**

rope, sparrows followed, always living close to man and largely dependent on him. As villages became towns and then cities, the sparrows survived because these new, dusty habitats were not so different from those arid conditions to which they were originally adapted. In the last century, house sparrows were introduced by European colonists to North and South America, South Africa, Australia and New Zealand; more recently they have spread across Siberia because of the agricultural development of the steppes.

The starling's invasion of towns began only about 150 years ago. However, starlings feed mainly on invertebrates in

Below: **A European garden. Most garden birds are woodland species.**

Wood Pigeon

House Martin

Bullfinch

Blue Tit

House Sparrow

Song Thrush

grassland and so cannot breed in cities except where there are parks and gardens with lawns. The greatest benefit they get from towns is in winter, when huge numbers fly in from their rural feeding grounds to gather on ledges, where the warmth generated from buildings and urban activities increase their chances of survival in cold conditions.

Rock doves may have first come into towns because man kept them for food. Later, they found that the buildings offered them an abundance of nesting ledges much like their ancestral cliffs. Now, in many cities, man feeds the pigeons not for food but for enjoyment.

Other natural cliff nesters such as martins, and hole nesters such as swifts, have benefitted by using buildings as nest sites. Most other urban birds either scavenge rubbish (like gulls and crows) or live in parks and gardens where the trees, shrubs and lawns create conditions similar to the edges of woodlands and are colonised by birds adapted to woodland life.

Below: **Some European blue tits pull the tops from milk bottles and drink the cream. This is an extension of their natural technique of seeking small insects beneath bark.**

Above: **Flocks of pigeons can be found in towns all over the world, in this case in Afghanistan.**

Below: **Most urban birds are either hole nesters, exploiting building ledges and cavities, or species which feed on wasted and spilled food, especially grain.**

Starlings space themselves out at about 10 centimetres apart when resting, close enough to jab at each other.

Jackdaw

Black Redstart

Collared Dove

Pied Wagtail

Birdwatching

Bird identification rapidly becomes easier with practice but at first even the common species will seem confusing. You will get a lot of help if you join a club or society and go on their outings. If you haven't the opportunity to do this, then concentrate initially on getting to know the birds that you see regularly around your home. When you know these twenty or thirty species fairly well and, given a reasonable view, can identify them quickly and confidently, they will provide a basis on which you can steadily extend your knowledge and identification skill.

If you wish to identify more than the few species that you will see close to, you will need binoculars. Magnification should be by 8 or 10 times, not the only factor to consider: cheap glasses with poor lenses may give poor performance. The best procedure is to go to a reputable binocular stockist and take his advice. You will be able to try out a wide variety of models and select one that best suits your requirements.

Some birds are very tame and confiding, but most are wary and should be approached with caution. In woodland, most small birds may prove very hard to watch, and one good technique is to sit quietly with your back to a tree on the edge of a clearing and wait for the birds to come to you. Another good place to watch is at water, where all birds will eventually come to drink and bathe. Open waters, mudflats, and salt marshes on estuaries often hold large numbers of birds but because there is little cover, the nearest birds will flush as soon as you get close and their alarm may cause the whole area to empty. So take advantage of cover such as sea walls or bankside vegetation, and keep off the skyline. Cars make excellent 'hides' from which to watch birds and have the added merits of keeping you warm and dry.

Respect birds' privacy at nesting time, be careful not to damage nests and vegetation as you go about your birdwatching, and obtain permission prior to crossing private land.

Gulls on a cliff face in the evening sunlight.

Bibliography

An Introduction to Ornithology, Wallace and Mahan, Macmillan 1975

Bird Flight, Georg Ruppel, Van Nostrand Reinhold Co. 1977

Birds: An Illustrated Survey, John Gooders, Hamlyn 1975

Birds and their World, John Andrews, Hamlyn 1976

Birds of Man's World, Derek Goodwin, Cornell University Press 1978

Birds of Paradise and Bower Birds, T Iredale, Georgian House Pty Ltd 1950

Birds of Prey: Their Biology and Ecology, Leslie Brown, Hamlyn 1976

Ducks, Geese and Swans of the World, P A Johnsgard, Univ. of Nebraska Press 1978

Ecological Adaptations for Breeding in Birds, David Lack, Methuen 1968

Evolutionary Biology of Animal Migration, R Robin Baker, 1978

Falcons of the World, J Cade, Collins 1982

Flamingos, Janet Kear and Nicole Duplaix-Hall, TAD Poyster 1975

Hamlyn Nature Guides: Birds, John Andrews, Hamlyn 1978

Hummingbirds, Walter Scheithauer, Arthur Barker 1967

Introduced Birds of the World, John L Lang, 1981

Owls: Their Natural and Unnatural History, John Sparks and Tony Soper, David and Charles 1970

Parent Birds and their Young, Alexander F Skutch, University of Texas Press 1976

Parrots of the World, J M Forshaw, David and Charles 1981

Plovers, Sandpipers and Snipes of the World, P A Johnsgard, Univ. of Nebraska Press 1981

Seabirds: Their Biology and Ecology, Bryan Nelson, Hamlyn 1980

The Biology of Penguins, Bernard Stonehouse, Macmillan 1975

The Life of Birds, Jean Dorst, Weidenfeld and Nicholson 1947

Vanishing Birds, Tim Halliday, Sidgwick and Jackson 1978

Index